THE TREATY, 1921 — RECORDS FROM THE ARCHIVES

The Treaty 1921

Records from the Archives

Edited by John Gibney and Zoë Reid

An Chartlann Náisiúnta
National Archives

Acadamh Ríoga na hÉireann
Royal Irish Academy

The Treaty, 1921: Records from the Archives

First published 2022

Royal Irish Academy, 19 Dawson Street, Dublin 2
www.ria.ie

Published in partnership with the National Archives, Ireland.
www.nationalarchives.ie

© National Archives and the authors

ISBN 978-1-911479-61-1 (PB)
ISBN 978-1-911479-62-8 (pdf)

British Library Cataloging in Publication Data.
A CIP catalogue record for this book is available from the British Library.

Publishing consultants: New Graphic
Designed by New Graphic
Proofread by Liz Evers
Printed in Ireland by Impress

Printed on Munken Lynx Rough 120gsm and 300gsm which is FSC-C020637, PEFC™ PEFC/05-33-99 certified.

Royal Irish Academy is a member of Publishing Ireland, the Irish book publishers' association

5 4 3 2 1

Published with support from the Department of Tourism, Culture, Arts, Gaeltacht, Sport and Media under the Decade of Cententaries 2012–2023 Programme.

**An Roinn Turasóireachta, Cultúir
Ealaíon, Gaeltachta, Spóirt agus Meán**
Department of Tourism, Culture,
Arts, Gaeltacht, Sport and Media

A note from the publisher
We want to offset the environmental impacts of carbon produced during the production of our books and journals. For the production of our books and journals this year we will plant 45 trees with Easy Treesie.

Contents

DECISIONS of the Cabinet Members of the Delegation
October 12th, 1921.

—————— " ——————

1.   <u>Members of regular staff</u> to be paid weekly by us .Amounts
      to be refunded later by Depart-
      ments.

2.   <u>Payment of Domestic staff</u> to be arranged by J.McGrath.

3.   <u>Salaries of Special Staff</u> :-

Fionan Lynch	per month	£50.
J.McGrath	" "	£50.
D McCarthy	" "	£40.
D.Robinson	" "	£45. 5/-

      M.Knightley £ 2.2.0 per day from
      Monday Oct 17th, as retainer,
      £5 now by way of gratuity.

4.   £10 to be given each Delegate for Personal Expenses on Oct.14th

5.   £10 per week to be paid to Mrs Duggan and expended at her dis-
      cretion in providing entertainment and amusement for the Lady
      staff.

Foreword

The National Archives preserves the memory of the state in the form of its records. It acquires and protects Ireland's public records, thereby ensuring their availability as a resource for all. These records relate to the social, cultural, economic and political history of the island of Ireland from the middle ages through to the establishment of the Irish Free State in 1922 and into the modern era.

Amongst its collections is perhaps the most famous document in Irish history: the Anglo-Irish Treaty of 1921. It was appropriate that the National Archives should mark the centenary of the signing of the Treaty by presenting a major exhibition of records in its possession relating to the negotiation and signing of the Treaty by the Irish delegation that travelled to London in October 1921. Using the Treaty itself as the centrepiece, this exhibition placed significant documents from the collections of the National Archives on public display for the first time to explore the Treaty negotiations and the experience of the Irish delegation through the documentary record that they left behind. This catalogue is based on the exhibition.

The exhibition and the associated catalogue, as presented here, form part of the National Archives Commemorations Programme 2021–2, marking the National Archives' role as the official repository of the records of the state. They have been presented in partnership with the Royal Irish Academy, whose Documents on Irish Foreign Policy (DIFP) project played a central role in developing the exhibition text and co-curating the structure and content for the exhibition and catalogue, the National Library of Ireland and the Office of Public Works, with records included from the collections of the Military Archives, Dublin, and University College Dublin Archives.

Orlaith McBride
Director, National Archives

Introduction
The Treaty negotiations: London, 11 October – 6 December 1921

To understand the Treaty and its significance, we need to glance back to the years prior to the outbreak of the First World War, when the island of Ireland as a whole formed part of the United Kingdom (UK). Irish political life was dominated at this time by nationalists demanding a limited form of self-government within the UK (known as Home Rule) and unionists who insisted on maintaining the political 'union' with Britain.

Alongside these, other political forces were gathering strength: separatist republicans seeking full independence, a suffrage movement demanding women's full political and social rights, and a labour movement seeking greater rights for Ireland's rural and urban working classes.

The prospect of Home Rule being implemented after 1912 nearly provoked a civil war between its supporters and Irish unionists (largely concentrated in the north-east of Ireland), who feared domination by the nationalist majority. The outbreak of war in Europe temporarily defused this conflict in Ireland, as Home Rule was postponed until after the end of the war. In April 1916 separatist republicans seized the opportunity to stage a rebellion, known as the Easter Rising, largely confined to Dublin, demanding Irish independence as a republic. In the years after the Easter Rising republicanism was revived as a meaningful political force and was represented by the political party Sinn Féin ('Ourselves'), originally founded in 1905 but reorganised after 1916 on a separatist platform.

The first post-war general election was held across the UK in December 1918 with more people eligible to vote than ever before, including, for the first time, some women over the age of thirty. Sinn Féin won 73 of Ireland's 105 UK parliamentary seats. The party boycotted Westminster and on 21 January 1919 its new representatives who were still at liberty assembled at Dublin's Mansion House as Dáil Éireann and declared Ireland independent. On the same day two police officers were killed in an ambush in County Tipperary by members of the paramilitary Irish Republican Army (IRA). The Irish War of Independence had begun: the Dáil devoted itself to securing recognition for Irish independence abroad and established its own administration to undermine British rule at home, while the IRA began a campaign of urban and rural guerrilla warfare across the island. The British authorities responded with reprisals and repression, by both military and paramilitary forces, and the conflict steadily became more intense and brutal throughout 1920 and early 1921.

Support for Home Rule had declined but in 1920 the British established two Home Rule parliaments: one in Belfast to govern six north-eastern counties and another in Dublin to govern the remaining twenty-six counties. Partition neutralised most unionist opposition to Irish self-government, but the British government recognised that a more substantial settlement would be needed with Sinn Féin as the War of Independence went on, and as British public opinion turned against military repression. Moves towards a truce intensified following the formal opening of the Northern Ireland parliament by King George V in June 1921, and the conflict formally came to a halt when a truce came into effect on 11 July 1921.

Within days exploratory talks took place in London between Éamon de Valera, as president of Dáil Éireann, and David Lloyd George, the British prime minister. In late September 1921 Lloyd George sent de Valera 'a fresh invitation to a conference in London on October 11th, where we can meet your delegates as spokesmen of the people whom you represent with a view to ascertaining how the association of Ireland with the community of nations known as the British Empire may best be reconciled with Irish national aspirations'. This invitation was accepted.

The formal negotiations and attendant discussions took place in a variety of locations in London: 10 Downing Street, the London premises of the Irish delegation at Hans Place in Knightsbridge, the Grosvenor Hotel and even the private residences of figures like Winston Churchill. The Irish negotiators were Arthur Griffith (Dáil Éireann's minister for foreign affairs, and the leader of the delegation), Robert Barton (minister for economic affairs), Michael Collins (minister for finance and IRA director of intelligence), Éamonn Duggan and George Gavan Duffy. The British negotiators were David Lloyd George (prime minister), Austen Chamberlain (lord privy seal), Winston Churchill (secretary of state for the colonies), Laming Worthington-Evans (secretary of state for war), Hamar Greenwood (chief secretary for Ireland), Gordon Hewart (attorney general), and F. E. Smith, Lord Birkenhead (lord chancellor).

Beginning on 11 October, the two sides met in plenary sessions until 24 October, after which the talks continued within sub-committees dealing with defence, finance and the maintenance of the truce. From this point on, Collins and Griffith did the bulk of the negotiating on the main issues. Controversially, Éamon de Valera remained in Dublin.

The plenipotentiaries (as they were designated) had been authorised by the Dáil to 'negotiate and conclude' a treaty, but their instructions from the Dáil Cabinet specified that they were to refer back to Dublin before making a final decision. This contradiction between the two sets of instructions became a source of tension as time went on, and the necessity to travel back and forth between London and Dublin became a gruelling obligation. While de Valera and the Irish negotiators certainly considered the possibility that he might join the talks in London, his absence meant that, while the British negotiators were led by the prime minister, the Irish team was not being led by his counterpart.

The British negotiators could draw upon a greater degree of political and negotiating experience and the machinery of their own bureaucracy and administration and had the advantage that the negotiations were taking place in London. The Irish delegation established their own base in London, divided between two townhouses: 22 Hans Place in Knightsbridge and 15 Cadogan Gardens in nearby Chelsea. The delegation itself was much larger than the five plenipotentiaries and included (amongst others) advisers, housekeepers, cooks and secretarial staff to undertake the extensive drafting of documents and press releases. Members of the IRA were also present to provide both security and a confidential means of communication with Ireland. An aircraft was even purchased to allow Collins and some of the delegation to make a quick getaway should negotiations break down. In the end, this was not needed.

The members of the Irish delegation were in the public eye as soon as they landed at Holyhead. When they arrived at Downing Street on 11 October they were met by crowds of well-wishers from London's Irish community, though it should be said that the delegation faced hostility from some quarters. The negotiations were covered extensively in the press (Collins was a particular source of fascination). The Irish offices were a magnet for journalists and a diverse range of visitors including literary luminaries such as George Bernard Shaw and Ezra Pound, but the presence of the Irish delegation in London had a serious purpose.

The British government was intent on securing a settlement of the so-called 'Irish question.' The principal issue of concern to them was Ireland's future relationship to the Crown and the British Empire, with naval defence, trade and finance being their other priorities.

For the Irish side, sovereignty and Irish unity were the critical issues. The Irish negotiators sought an outcome suggested by de Valera in which Ireland would 'become an external associate of the states of the British Commonwealth' rather than a full member. It was a strategy that implicitly conceded that they were not going to return from London with a fully independent republic. Instead, as Thomas Jones, the deputy secretary to the British Cabinet, had earlier noted, 'they seemed to think of a republic within the Empire' (a concept successfully revived in the 1930s, but which proved unacceptable to the British negotiators in 1921).

Any Irish willingness to accept a formal relationship with the Crown depended on securing concessions on the partition of Ireland. Northern Ireland had been established in May 1921. The Ulster Unionist leader James Craig, as prime minister of Northern Ireland, had enough political support in London to ignore suggestions that he make concessions towards Irish unity. Lloyd George, as a Liberal prime minister at the head of a coalition dominated by the Conservative Party, was acutely aware any attempt to pressurise Ulster unionism was a step too far for Tories. He secured a commitment from Arthur Griffith to consider a proposal that Northern Ireland would have a right to vote itself out of a prospective all-Ireland parliament, and that a 'boundary commission' could then adjudicate on the border. This was originally given to protect Lloyd George from potential critics within the Conservative Party but was ultimately used to remove any prospect of the Irish plenipotentiaries breaking off the negotiations over the issue of partition.

Partition is often assumed to have been the main point of contention in the negotiations, but sovereignty was the central issue for both sides. The British intended to maintain the integrity of an empire that, unlike many of its counterparts, had emerged victorious from the cataclysm of the First World War. The complete 'secession' of a substantial portion of the UK was never going to be acceptable to the British in these circumstances, nor was the idea that Ireland become semi-detached from the empire by what was termed an 'external association'. The Irish plenipotentiaries were in no position to bridge the gap between their stance and that of the British. While the British made various concessions to the Irish towards the end of the talks, they forced the Irish to agree to the Treaty with a warning from Lloyd George 'that those who were not for peace must take full responsibility for the war that would immediately follow refusal by any Delegate to sign the Articles of Agreement.'

The eventual Treaty created the Irish Free State as a 'dominion' with the same constitutional status as Canada. Its terms proved sufficiently divisive to lead to a bitter and devastating civil war in Ireland from June 1922 onwards, but this could not be foreseen with certainty on 6 December 1921, and the original exhibition, as reflected in this catalogue, was not concerned with events after the signing of the Treaty. Like the exhibition upon which it is based, this catalogue explores the paths that led to the Treaty, and opens a window into the world in which the Irish delegation operated during their time in London. It does so through the documentary record that they left behind, much of it drafted by secretarial staff like Kathleen McKenna and Lily O'Brennan and retained by the National Archives in Dublin and other archives in Ireland. The documents that follow are presented in order to cast light on the outcomes that the Irish negotiators sought and on the choices that they were presented with; their own words are the surest guide.

John Gibney
Assistant Editor, Documents on Irish Foreign Policy (DIFP), Royal Irish Academy. The DIFP series publishes archival material relating to Ireland's foreign relations since 1919 and is a partnership project of the Royal Irish Academy, the National Archives and the Department of Foreign Affairs. **www.difp.ie**

The Irish revolution:
a political timeline from
Home Rule to truce

Before the outbreak of the First World War in 1914 Ireland
was part of the United Kingdom of Great Britain and Ireland
(UK). Irish political life was dominated at this time by
nationalists demanding a limited form of self-government
within the UK ('Home Rule'), and unionists insisting on
maintaining the political 'union' with Britain.

Crowds assembled on Dublin's Westland Row in
1917 to welcome the return of republican prisoners
detained in Britain after the Easter Rising of 1916.

Courtesy of the National Library of Ireland. KE128

1912–14

The prospect of Home Rule being implemented in 1912 nearly provoked a civil war between its supporters and Irish unionists, largely concentrated in the northern province of Ulster, who feared domination by the nationalist majority. The partition of Ireland into separate jurisdictions was proposed by Britain as a solution.

The unionist leader Sir Edward Carson inspects members of the Ulster Volunteer Force which had been established by unionists in Ulster opposed to Home Rule, c. 1913–14.

Courtesy of the National Library of Ireland. HOG 240

1914–16

The outbreak of war in Europe temporarily defused the possibility of a conflict in Ireland as Home Rule was postponed until after the end of the war. In April 1916 militant separatists staged a rebellion – the Easter Rising – demanding Irish independence as a republic. It was swiftly suppressed by Britain. One of the separatist groups involved in the Rising – the Irish Volunteers – later evolved into the IRA.

The ruins of Dublin's Sackville Street (O'Connell Street) after the Easter Rising.

Courtesy of the National Library of Ireland. KE119

Constance Markievicz addresses a Sinn Féin election rally in Kilkenny, July 1917.

1917–18

After the Easter Rising separatist republicanism was revived as a meaningful political force. In the aftermath of the First World War a general election was held across the UK in December 1918. More people were eligible to vote than ever before, including, for the first time, some women over the age of 30. The separatist Sinn Féin party won 73 of Ireland's 105 UK parliamentary seats. The pro-Home Rule Irish Parliamentary Party was swept aside. Unionism remained the dominant political force in Ulster.

1919

Sinn Féin boycotted the UK parliament at Westminster, and on 21 January 1919 those of its newly elected representatives still at liberty convened in Dublin as Dáil Éireann. Instead of describing themselves as members of parliament (MPs), the members of the Dáil described themselves as 'teachtaí Dála' (TDs, meaning deputies to the Dáil). They declared Ireland independent and committed themselves to seeking international recognition for an independent Irish republic. On the same day two police officers were killed in an ambush in County Tipperary by members of the IRA. This incident is usually considered the beginning of the Irish War of Independence.

A contemporary poster depicting the meeting of the first Dáil Éireann in the Mansion House, Dublin, 21 January 1919 , with the central photograph surrounded by portrait images of those elected as TDs.

Courtesy of the National Library of Ireland. PD D40

British troops patrolling the streets of an unidentified Irish town during the War of Independence, c.1920.

Courtesy of the National Library of Ireland. INDH31D

1920

The War of Independence intensified. With unionists still opposed to Irish self-government or independence, Britain established two Home Rule parliaments: one in Belfast to govern six north-eastern counties, now called 'Northern Ireland', and another in Dublin to govern the remaining 26 counties of 'Southern Ireland'. Ireland was now partitioned into two jurisdictions.

1921

A truce between the IRA and British forces came into effect on 11 July.

Crowds gathered outside Dublin's Mansion House awaiting news of the impending truce, July 1921.

Courtesy of the National Library of Ireland. HOG116

Truce

The Irish War of Independence was formally brought to a halt by the truce that came into effect on 11 July 1921.

The Irish revolution occurred in a world that had been turned upside down by the First World War. After the war, Britain had extensive military commitments in Europe and across its global empire. With Britain under increased international scrutiny, particularly in the United States of America, it had become, by mid-1921, too difficult practically and politically to sustain its campaign against Sinn Féin and the IRA. The truce and the negotiations that led to the Treaty were the consequence.

Typescript memorandum dated 9 July 1921 with the proposed terms of the truce that came into effect on 11 July 1921.

NAI DE/2/247/16

9.7.21.

MEMO.

_____

R.I.C and Auxiliary Police

1. No incoming troops ∕ and munitions, and no movements for military
purposes of troops and munitions, ~~except maintenance draft~~,

2. No provocative displays of forces armed or unarmed.

3. It is understood that all provisions of this truce apply to the
Martial Law area equally with the rest of Ireland.

4. No pursuit of Irish officers, men, war material, or military
stores.

5. No secret agents, noting desctiptions or movements, and no
interference with the movements of Irish persons, military or civil,
and no attempt to discover the haunts or habits of Irish officers
and men.

   <u>Note</u>: This supposes the abandonment of Curfew restrictions.

6. No pursuit or observance of lines of communications or connection.

7. No pursuit of messengers.

8. No Courts Martial of Irish prisoners in jail.

9. No other trials of Irish prisoners in jail.

~~10~~ 8. No interference with motor or bicycle traffic, or any other
traffic coming under the scope of present regulations.

   <u>Note</u>: This means that the present regulations become inoperative
from the period of cessation of hostilities. Also that there must
be no insistance upon permits, whether drivers' permits or owners'
permits.

11. Suspension generally of the R.O.I.R.

X *handed over for further consideration*

   Note. *There are other details connected with Courts Martial
   & Motor Permits to be agreed to later.*

Draft by Michael Collins

and no movement
for military purp[oses]
of troops or m[en]

Army

displays of any
forces —

1. No incoming troops
   and munitions

2. " pursuit of men
   or munition

3. " pursuit of lines
   of connection

4. " [movement] of
   messengers

5. " Secret Agents
   noting descriptions
   or movements

6. No procurators

7. No Courts Martial
   of Irish
   prisoners in Jail

8. No other trials
   of Irish Prisoners
   in Jail

9. No difference in
   the status of
   Martial Law Area and the rest of Ireland

10. Abandonment of Mo[...]
    + any other tra[...]

and no interference
with movement
of Irish troops
persons military
or civil

'Our nation has formally declared its independence and recognises itself as a sovereign State.'

Éamon de Valera to David Lloyd George, 12 September 1921
Official correspondence relating to the peace negotiations June–September 1921 (Dublin, 1921)

Handwritten draft by Michael Collins of proposed truce terms, 9 July 1921.

NAI DE/2/247/17

The preliminary negotiations, July–September 1921

Three days after the truce, Éamon de Valera, president of Dáil Éireann, met British prime minister David Lloyd George at 10 Downing Street in London for exploratory talks towards a potential Anglo-Irish settlement.

Crowds of supporters from London's Irish community greeted the Irish leader at Euston Station and recited the rosary at the entrance to Downing Street in Whitehall. Lloyd George waited, filled with anxious excitement, for de Valera to arrive at 4.30pm on 14 July. They met four times unaccompanied between 14 and 21 July, sizing up each other and their positions.

On 20 July the British government set out its principal issues of concern and proposed Irish membership of the British Empire as a self-governing 'dominion'. Dublin held to its demand for unrestricted independence; the British proposals were rejected on 10 August and the future of the talks looked doubtful. Through de Valera, the concept of 'external association' began to emerge. This formula envisaged an independent Ireland that internally would be a republic, but which would be associated or aligned with the British Empire for certain defence and foreign-policy matters.

Contacts were maintained between the two sides. While on holidays in Gairloch in the Scottish Highlands, Lloyd George wrote to de Valera on 29 September to invite Irish representatives to a conference in London to negotiate a settlement. The invitation was accepted, and de Valera and his colleagues began to appoint their negotiators.

From left to right: Arthur Griffith, Robert Barton, Laurence O'Neill,
Count George Noble Plunkett and Éamon de Valera, pictured at Dún Laoghaire
prior to departing for London for preliminary talks with the British government
following the truce of July 1921. Plunkett was officially the Dáil's foreign minister
at this time, but his hands-on involvement in its activities was minimal.

Courtesy of the Military Archives, Dublin

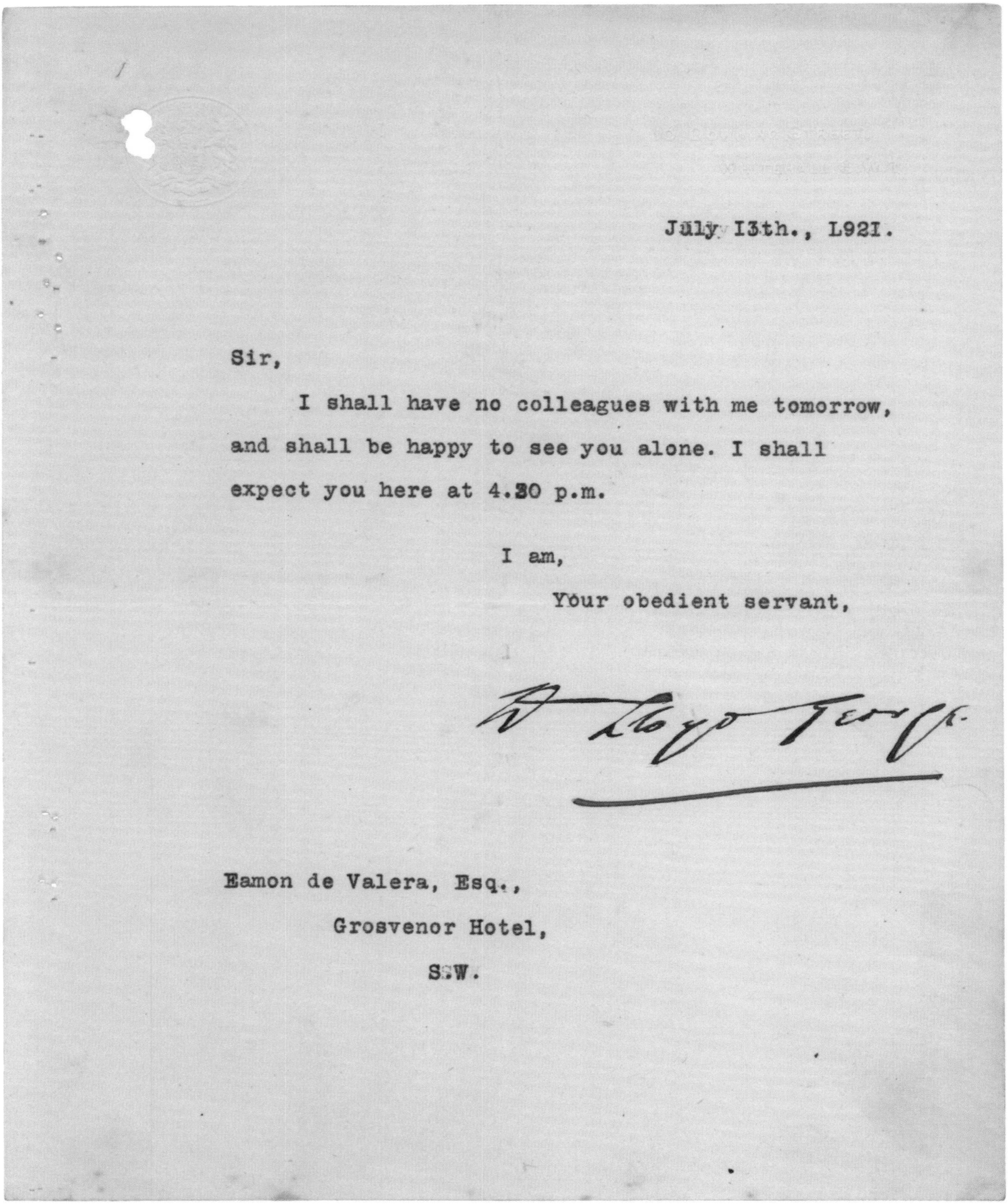

July 13th., 1921.

Sir,

I shall have no colleagues with me tomorrow, and shall be happy to see you alone. I shall expect you here at 4.30 p.m.

I am,

Your obedient servant,

D Lloyd George.

Eamon de Valera, Esq.,
Grosvenor Hotel,
S.W.

A note from David Lloyd George to Éamon de Valera, agreeing to the latter's request that they meet each other unaccompanied. They met for the first time the following day, 14 July 1921.

NAI DE/2/302/249

Sympathisers and supporters from London's Irish community gather outside Downing Street during de Valera's talks with Lloyd George, 14 July 1921. Those kneeling at the front are praying, with rosary beads visible on the left.

Courtesy of the National Library of Ireland. HOGW 1

The Irish delegation that travelled to London in July 1921, pictured in the Grosvenor Hotel, London. Seated, left to right: Éamon de Valera and Arthur Griffith. Standing, middle row, left to right: Count George Noble Plunkett, Laurence O'Neill, Lily O'Brennan, Lora Farnan, Kathleen O'Connell. Standing, back row, left to right: Erskine Childers, Dr Robert Farnan, Robert Barton.

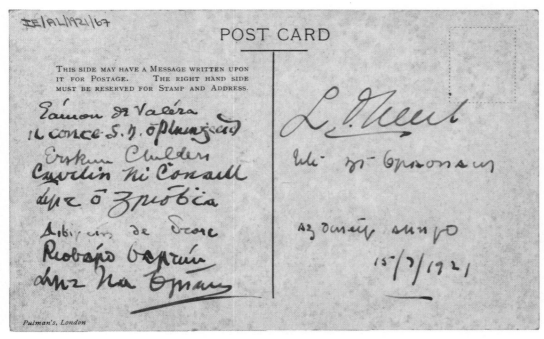

Colour postcard of the Grosvenor Hotel, London, autographed by
some of those present in London for discussions with the British in
July 1921. Most signed with the Irish versions of their names: Éamon
de Valera, Count George Plunkett, Erskine Childers, Kathleen
O'Connell, Arthur Griffith, Austin Stack, Robert Barton, Art O'Brien,
Laurence O'Neill, Lily O'Brennan. 'Dining here 15/7/1921.'

Courtesy of the Military Archives, Dublin

DAIL EIREANN.

OFFICIAL CORRESPONDENCE

RELATING TO THE

PEACE NEGOTIATIONS

JUNE–SEPTEMBER, 1921.

PART I.

Preliminary Correspondence, June 24th to July 9th, 1921.

PART II.

Correspondence arising from the Conversations at London, between
President de Valera and the British Prime Minister
July 20th to September 30th.

DUBLIN, OCTOBER, 1921.

A copy of *Official correspondence relating to
the peace negotiations June–September, 1921*
(Dublin, 1921), published by Dáil Éireann.

NAI PRIV 1093/4/34

Timothy A Smiddy

CORRESPONDENCE

RELATING TO THE

PROPOSALS OF HIS MAJESTY'S GOVERNMENT FOR AN IRISH SETTLEMENT.

Presented to Parliament by Command of His Majesty.

LONDON:
PRINTED AND PUBLISHED BY
HIS MAJESTY'S STATIONERY OFFICE.

To be purchased through any Bookseller or directly from
H.M. STATIONERY OFFICE at the following addresses:
IMPERIAL HOUSE, KINGSWAY, LONDON, W.C.2, and 28, ABINGDON STREET, LONDON, S.W.1;
37, PETER STREET, MANCHESTER; 1, ST. ANDREW'S CRESCENT, CARDIFF;
23, FORTH STREET, EDINBURGH;
or from E. PONSONBY, LTD., 116, GRAFTON STREET, DUBLIN.

1921.

[Cmd. 1502.] *Price 1d. Net.*

A copy of *Correspondence relating to the proposals of His Majesty's government for an Irish settlement* (London, 1921), containing British proposals for a settlement and subsequent correspondence between Éamon de Valera and David Lloyd George. This copy is signed by Timothy A. Smiddy, professor of economics at University College Cork, who served as an economic advisor to the Treaty delegation in London.

NAI PRIV 1093/4/35

'We, therefore, send you herewith a fresh invitation to a conference in London on October 11th, where we can meet your delegates as spokesmen of the people whom you represent with a view to ascertaining how the association of Ireland with the community of nations known as the British Empire may best be reconciled with Irish national aspirations.'

David Lloyd George to Éamon de Valera, 29 September 1921
Official correspondence relating to the peace negotiations June–September 1921 (Dublin, 1921)

Crowds greet Éamon de Valera at Dún Laoghaire following his return from London, July 1921.

Courtesy of the National Library of Ireland. HOGW58

The Irish delegation

The Irish delegation that went to London in October 1921 was led by Arthur Griffith, Dáil Éireann's minister for foreign affairs.

Griffith was joined by Michael Collins, the Dáil Éireann minister for finance who also held key positions in the IRA and in the militant and conspiratorial Irish Republican Brotherhood (IRB), the group that had organised the Easter Rising. As Griffith's de facto second-in-command in London and the man many viewed as effectively the leader of the IRA, Collins was in the limelight. He saw himself as a soldier and had not wanted to join the delegation.

Griffith and Collins were accompanied by three other negotiators: George Gavan Duffy, Robert Barton and Éamonn Duggan. Duffy was an experienced lawyer who had been one of Dáil Éireann's emissaries in Paris and Rome. Robert Barton, Dáil Éireann's minister for economic development, and Éamonn Duggan, a solicitor closely associated with Sinn Féin, had been signatories of the July 1921 truce. Duggan was the chief Irish liaison officer with the British for the implementation of the truce.

The Irish delegation included a secretariat, headed by Erskine Childers, and other support staff. These men and women included political, legal, economic and military counsellors and publicity advisers, along with housekeepers and cooks (apparently including staff from Dublin's Gresham Hotel).

Members of the IRA provided security and, as couriers, a confidential means of communication with Ireland. The secretarial staff undertook the drafting of press releases and the extensive documentation required by the Irish negotiators. Many others came and went as the need arose. The Irish delegation was not isolated in London as there was constant travel back and forth along a well-established route to Ireland.

Members of the Treaty delegation in 22 Hans Place, Knightsbridge, just after their arrival in London. Back row, left to right: Michael Knightly, John Chartres, George Gavan Duffy, Robert Barton, Éamonn Duggan, Arthur Griffith, Erskine Childers. Seated, far left: Joseph McGrath, D. L. Robinson. Leaning forward, far right: Fionán Lynch. Front, left to right: Lily O'Brennan, Ellie Lyons, May Duggan, Bridget Lynch, Kathleen McKenna, Alice Lyons.

Courtesy of the National Library of Ireland. MS 49,835/15/8

Arthur Griffith

Arthur Griffith (1871–1922) was born in Dublin. Originally a printer, he moved into journalism while living in South Africa. On returning to Dublin in 1898 he established himself as an energetic journalist and prominent nationalist activist with a particular interest in economic independence. In 1904 he published *The Resurrection of Hungary*, in which he advocated a form of Irish independence under a monarchy shared with Britain (an idea modelled on the Austro-Hungarian Empire). In 1905 he founded the political party Sinn Féin (Ourselves). It failed to gain much support at this time, but Griffith remained an influential voice among radical nationalists.

Griffith played no part in the Easter Rising but was interned in the aftermath, being released in December 1916. One of Griffith's key ideas was that Irish MPs should withdraw from Westminster and establish their own assembly in Ireland. As Sinn Féin was revived as a vehicle for separatism, Griffith was elected as abstentionist MP for Cavan East in a by-election in June 1918, despite having been imprisoned again before the election. After his release in April 1919 he became Dáil Éireann's minister for home affairs. Griffith was second only to Éamon de Valera at the head of Sinn Féin and in July 1921 he accompanied de Valera to London for preliminary discussions with the British. Griffith became the Dáil's minister for foreign affairs in August 1921 and in October was appointed chairman of the Irish delegation that was to negotiate the Treaty.

Courtesy of the National Library of Ireland. KE238

Robert C. Barton

Courtesy of the National Library of Ireland. INDH94

Robert Childers Barton (1881–1975) was born into a landed family in County Wicklow. He was educated in England at Rugby School, Warwickshire, then Christ Church, Oxford, and at the Royal Agricultural College in Gloucestershire.

Barton was a supporter of Home Rule and joined the Irish Volunteers in 1913. Following the outbreak of the First World War he enlisted in the Royal Dublin Fusiliers and served in Dublin during the suppression of the Easter Rising, after which he resigned his commission and became involved in separatist politics. He was elected as abstentionist Sinn Féin MP for Wicklow West in the December 1918 election and took his seat as a TD in the first Dáil Éireann, where he was appointed minister for agriculture.

In February 1919 he was arrested for making a seditious speech at Carnew, County Wicklow; he escaped, but was rearrested in January 1920. He was released in July 1921 just prior to the truce and accompanied Éamon de Valera to London later that month. Barton was elected to the second Dáil for Kildare-Wicklow, becoming minister for economic affairs. He was selected as a member of the delegation that travelled to London in October due to his expertise in economics. In London, his relations with Arthur Griffith were tense, and Lloyd George took a dismissive view of him. Barton was one of the three plenipotentiaries present in the final meeting with the British delegation at which the Treaty was agreed and signed.

39

Michael Collins

Michael Collins (1890–1922) was born in Woodfield, County Cork. He moved to London aged fifteen where he worked in various clerical roles for nine years, gaining invaluable administrative experience. While in London he joined the Gaelic Athletic Association (GAA) and the Gaelic League and was sworn into the IRB in 1909, eventually becoming IRB treasurer for southern England.

He joined the Irish Volunteers in 1914 and returned to Ireland in January 1916. He served in Dublin's General Post Office (GPO) during the Easter Rising as aide-de-camp to Joseph Mary Plunkett and was interned in Frongoch, Wales, for his involvement. His rise to prominence as one of a new generation of republican leaders began in captivity. Collins became a key figure in the reorganisation of the Irish Volunteers, and to a lesser extent Sinn Féin, in the years after 1916. He sat as TD for Cork South in the first Dáil and became Dáil minister for finance in April 1919, overseeing the Dáil loan to raise funds for the independence movement. Later that year he became president of the supreme council of the IRB, and succeeded Éamonn Duggan as director of intelligence of the IRA.

He was not present for the talks in London in July 1921 between Éamon de Valera and Lloyd George and reluctantly accepted his appointment as one of the plenipotentiaries for the negotiations in October. The British side found him to be a more pragmatic and flexible negotiator than they had expected.

Courtesy of the National Library of Ireland. NPA POLF45

George Gavan Duffy

Courtesy of the Military Archives, Dublin

George Gavan Duffy (1882–1951) was born in Rock Ferry, Cheshire. Educated in England and France, he qualified as a solicitor in London in 1907 and acted for Roger Casement during his trial for treason in 1916. The trial had an enormous impact on Duffy, and soon after, he moved to Ireland. He was called to the Irish Bar in 1917 and became heavily involved in Irish political life. He sat as Sinn Féin TD for Dublin County South in the first Dáil.

Duffy was, along with Seán T. Ó Ceallaigh, one of the emissaries sent by the Dáil to Paris to lobby the post-war peace conference to recognise Irish independence (they were unsuccessful), and to disseminate propaganda in support of the Irish cause. He subsequently carried out a similar role in Rome.

His legal expertise was the basis for his appointment in October 1921 as one of the Irish plenipotentiaries in London. His relations with Michael Collins and Arthur Griffith were tense. Duffy did not believe Lloyd George's threat of renewed war if the proposed Treaty terms were not accepted but felt obliged to sign the Treaty because the other plenipotentiaries had all done so.

Éamonn J. Duggan

Éamonn John Duggan (1874/9–1936) was born in Longwood, County Meath. He worked as a law clerk before becoming a solicitor in 1914 and establishing a practice in Dublin city centre. Duggan joined the Irish Volunteers in 1914 and fought in the Easter Rising as a member of Edward Daly's staff at the North Dublin Union and later at Father Mathew Hall on Church Street. He was sentenced to three years' penal servitude for his role in the Rising but was released in June 1917 and resumed his legal practice.

He acted for the family of Thomas Ashe following the latter's death after he had been force fed while on hunger strike. Duggan was a member of the IRB and became director of intelligence for the IRA in May 1918. He sat as Sinn Féin TD for Meath South in the first Dáil and read the declaration of independence at its inaugural meeting in January 1919.

Duggan was arrested in November 1920 and was jailed in Mountjoy Prison in Dublin along with Arthur Griffith before being transferred to Brixton Prison in London. While in prison he became involved in efforts to broker a truce. After his release in June 1921 Duggan was appointed chief Irish liaison officer with the British to oversee the truce. He accompanied Éamon de Valera to the talks with David Lloyd George in London that July. Duggan was appointed in October as one of the five plenipotentiaries and he played an important role in keeping open channels of communication with senior British officials. He remained a supporter of Collins and Griffith throughout the negotiations.

Courtesy of the Military Archives, Dublin.

John Smith Chartres

John Smith Chartres (1862–1927) was born in Birkenhead, Cheshire. He was educated at Wellington College, Berkshire, the University of London, the King's Inns, Dublin, and in Germany. In 1904 Chartres was appointed the first head of *The Times's* intelligence (research, indexing and reference) department and became an economic correspondent for the *Daily Graphic* in 1914.

During the First World War he worked in the intelligence and records section of the ministry of munitions, before moving to the ministry of labour after the war. In 1917 Chartres met Arthur Griffith and soon after began contributing articles to Griffith's newspaper *Nationality*. He also became involved in gun-running for Michael Collins, and later became an informant for him.

Chartres had been transferred to Ireland, but resigned from the civil service in June 1921 due to his growing involvement in the Irish independence movement. Appointed Dáil Éireann envoy to Berlin, Chartres was, a few months later, appointed second secretary to the Treaty delegation. He participated in the plenary conferences and drafted numerous substantial memoranda for the delegation on key issues. Given his legal training, Chartres drafted proposed terms for Ireland's constitutional relationship with the British Crown. He lobbied strongly in favour of the concept of 'external association', as devised by Éamon de Valera. Chartres left London before the Treaty was signed.

(Robert) Erskine Childers

(Robert) Erskine Childers (1870–1922) was born in London. Educated at Cambridge, he was appointed joint assistant clerk at the House of Commons in January 1895 and served as an artillery driver in the Second Boer War.

In 1903 he found success as a novelist with the spy thriller *The Riddle of the Sands*. Childers became a supporter of Home Rule for Ireland and resigned his position at the House of Commons in October 1910. In 1914 he was one of the organisers of the Howth gun-running on behalf of the Irish Volunteers, and his yacht *Asgard* was used to smuggle the weapons. During the First World War Childers was an intelligence officer in the Royal Naval Air Service and later, after its formation, the Royal Air Force. In July 1917 he had served as assistant secretary to the Irish Convention.

Childers moved to Ireland in March 1919 and became a propagandist for Sinn Féin, a role he also briefly fulfilled in Paris later that year. He subsequently worked on Dáil Éireann's propaganda organ, the *Irish Bulletin*, and in February 1921 became the IRA's director of propaganda. Childers was close to Éamon de Valera and accompanied him to London in July 1921. He was subsequently appointed as one of the secretaries to the Irish delegation. Arthur Griffith disliked and distrusted him, and the British side viewed Childers as a malign influence. At the end of the negotiations he tried to discourage his cousin Robert Barton from signing the Treaty.

Diarmuid O'Hegarty

Fionán Lynch

Diarmuid O'Hegarty (1892–1958) was born in Skibbereen, County Cork. He attended school in Cork city and joined the civil service in 1910, working in the department of agriculture and technical instruction.

O'Hegarty joined the Keating Branch of the Gaelic League and was a member of the IRB. He fought in the Easter Rising and was briefly imprisoned in Knutsford Prison in Cheshire before being released by mistake. He became deeply involved in the reorganisation of the Irish Volunteers and the IRB. He was dismissed from his civil service post in 1918 for his refusal to take the oath of allegiance.

O'Hegarty was clerk of the first Dáil and secretary to the Dáil Cabinet, where his administrative skills proved invaluable as he dealt with the underground government's correspondence. He was a close associate of Michael Collins. Like Collins he occupied senior roles in various organisations: Dáil Éireann itself, the IRB, and the IRA, in which he served as director of communications from July 1918 and of organisation from March 1920.

Resigning from his IRA role in April 1921, O'Hegarty focused on his Dáil secretariat responsibilities. His experience and connections made him a natural choice as one of the secretaries to the Irish delegation in London.

Fionán Lynch (1889–1966) was born in Caherciveen, County Kerry. He attended University College Dublin and St Patrick's College, Drumcondra, where he qualified as a teacher. His first job was in Swansea, Wales, where he taught Irish and established a branch of the Gaelic League.

Lynch returned to Dublin in 1912 and became an active member of the staunchly republican Keating Branch of the Gaelic League. He joined the IRB and the Irish Volunteers, and, as a founding member of the dramatic society Na hAisteoirí, he helped produce plays in Irish throughout the country.

He fought in the Easter Rising and was imprisoned in Lewes, Sussex, until June 1917. After his release he resumed his involvement in separatism and was imprisoned for making a seditious speech in August 1917, after which he went on hunger strike alongside Thomas Ashe in Mountjoy Prison. Released in November 1917, Lynch was imprisoned again in May 1918 during the so-called 'German Plot' arrests. While still in captivity he was elected to the first Dáil as Sinn Féin TD for Kerry South. He was released in August 1919 and was elected TD for Kerry-Limerick West in the second Dáil, before being appointed assistant secretary to the Treaty delegation. Lynch played a significant role in organising the living arrangements for the delegation in London.

Kathleen McKenna

Elizabeth ('Lily') O'Brennan

Kathleen McKenna (1897–1988) was born in Oldcastle, County Meath. She briefly attended University College Dublin (UCD), but in March 1916 her family moved to Rugby, Warwickshire, where she worked as a secretary in an engineering firm. While visiting Dublin in the summer of 1919 McKenna presented herself at the Sinn Féin offices on Harcourt Street with a letter of introduction from her father to Arthur Griffith, stating that she wanted to play a role in the independence movement.

She worked in the Sinn Féin press bureau for the remainder of her holiday and in November 1919 McKenna joined the staff of the Dáil's newly established propaganda organ, the *Irish Bulletin*. This was a news-sheet printed in a variety of locations across Dublin and circulated five times per week by post, mainly to sympathetic journalists and opposition politicians in Britain. McKenna typed the text, often generated the copy and helped to oversee its distribution.

McKenna also acted as a confidential messenger for both the Dáil and the IRA. After the truce she joined the secretarial staff of the Dáil Cabinet at the Mansion House, while continuing to be involved in the production of the *Irish Bulletin* for the Dáil's publicity department. McKenna became, in October 1921, a member of the Irish delegation to the Treaty negotiations as Griffith's private secretary.

Elizabeth ('Lily') O'Brennan (1878–1948) was born in Dublin. She trained as a schoolteacher and with her sister Áine Ceannt attended the first meeting of Cumann na mBan (The Irishwomen's Council) in Dublin in April 1914.

During the Easter Rising O'Brennan and other members of Cumann na mBan were part of the Marrowbone Lane garrison in Dublin, under the overall command of Áine's husband Éamonn Ceannt. O'Brennan was active in the reorganisation of Cumann na mBan after 1916. From 1917 onwards she was a member of its executive and was acting secretary from 1918.

She was active in the Irish Republican Prisoners' Dependents' Fund, and in 1920 worked for the Dáil's minister for labour, Constance Markievicz, and oversaw an employment bureau for IRA members who had lost their jobs due to their activities. O'Brennan also acted as a courier, carried out some intelligence work for Michael Collins, and secured accommodation for IRA members on the run.

In February 1921 O'Brennan became Erskine Childers' private secretary when he was appointed as Dáil minister for publicity, and in this capacity was part of the Treaty delegation in London.

Gertrude ('Gerty') Conry

Ellie and Alice Lyons

Gertrude Conry (1892–1970) was born in County Mayo. Educated in Dublin and Bray, she joined the Dáil secretariat after the truce of 1921, working under Diarmuid O'Hegarty.

Conry accompanied the Irish delegation to London as O'Hegarty's private secretary. He apparently wanted the more experienced members of his staff to remain in Dublin to ensure that the Dáil administration could continue to function.

Conry travelled to London with the second contingent of the delegation on 9 October 1921. In London she shared a room with Kathleen McKenna. McKenna left a vivid account of how at night they both recited the rosary for the success of the Irish negotiators, to counter the mounting tension of the final weeks.

Ellie Lyons (1889–1973) and her sister Alice Lyons (1893–1974) were born in Dublin. Ellie had been working as a shorthand typist from at least 1911 and in 1920 both she and Alice joined the Dáil ministry for finance as typists.

Their cousin Eibhlin Lawless had worked as a stenographer for Michael Collins but resigned to become a nun; her father Frank, a member of the IRB, recommended his nieces as replacements.

Alice Lyons became Collins' private secretary, and her aptitude and composure were rated highly by contemporaries. During one British raid on Dáil offices in Dublin's Mary Street after the burning of the Custom House in May 1921, Alice escaped capture by calmly opting to leave as the raid was beginning, giving rise to a rumour that Collins himself had escaped disguised as a woman.

Collins was sufficiently impressed by both sisters to include them on the secretarial staff of the Treaty delegation, where they became close to Kathleen McKenna. In London, a photograph of the three was published in the press after waiting journalists insisted that they pose with a cat.

Alice Lyons shared an office with Diarmaid O'Hegarty at Cadogan Gardens. After the signing of the Treaty, the Lyons sisters, along with Kathleen McKenna, were tasked with staying on in London to clear any remaining documentation from the offices of the delegation before returning home to Dublin.

The instructions
to the delegation

The Irish negotiators were designated as 'plenipotentiaries' and had been authorised by the Dáil to conclude a treaty with Britain.

Instructions from the Dáil's ruling body – the Cabinet headed by de Valera, of which some of the plenipotentiaries were also members – confirmed the plenipotentiaries' authority but also specified that they were to communicate with the Dáil Cabinet and await a reply before making any final decision to conclude an agreement. These instructions also stated that any final draft text must be submitted to Dublin before signature. One set of instructions seemed to give the delegation authority to conclude an agreement, but the other did not. This contradiction became a source of tension as time went on.

De Valera was not part of the delegation that went to London. He argued that his presence in Dublin gave the Irish delegation an advantage as the necessity to consult with him in Dublin offered a last line of defence against British pressure. That said, he informed Griffith that he would consider going to London if it were deemed absolutely necessary. Some in the Irish delegation increasingly thought that de Valera should join them, but he remained in Ireland. While the British negotiators were led by the prime minister, the head of the British government, the Irish delegation was not led by his nominal opposite number.

Typescript document dated 7 October 1921 containing five points regarding the Irish negotiators' powers and obligations, notably the requirement to refer final decisions to the Dáil Cabinet in Dublin.

NAI DE4/5/1

Dáil Éireann.

Oifig an Rúnaíde
Secretariat Department

7th October, 1921.

INSTRUCTIONS TO PLENIPOTENTIARIES

FROM · CABINET.

(1) The Plenipotentiaries have full powers as defined in their credentials.

(2) It is understood however that before decisions are finally reached on the main questions that a despatch notifying the intention of making these decisions will be sent to the Members of the Cabinet in Dublin and that a reply will be awaited by the Plenipotentiaries before the final decision is made.

(3) It is also understood that the complete text of the draft treaty about to be signed will be similarly submitted to Dublin and reply awaited.

(4) In case of break the text of final proposals from our side will be similarly submitted.

(5) It is understood that the Cabinet in Dublin will be kept regularly informed of the progress of the negotiations.

----------oOo----------

TO ALL TO WHOM THESE PRESENTS COME, GREETING:

In virtue of the authority vested in me by
DAIL EIREANN, I hereby appoint

Arthur Griffith, T.D., Minister for Foreign Affairs, Chairman.

Michael Collins, T.D., Minister of Finance,

Robert C. Barton, T.D., Minister for Economic Affairs,

Edmund J. Duggan, T.D.,

George Gavan Duffy, T.D.

as Envoys Plenipotentiary from the Elected Government of the
REPUBLIC OF IRELAND to negotiate and conclude on behalf of
Ireland with the representatives of his Britannic Majesty,
GEORGE V., a Treaty or Treaties of Settlement, Association
and Accommodation between Ireland and the community of nations
known as the British Commonwealth.

IN WITNESS WHEREOF I hereunto subscribe my name
as President.

Done in the City of Dublin

Éamon de Valera

this 7th day of October in

the year of our Lord 1921

in five identical originals.

3- R.B.

DO CHUM GACH A BHFEICFIDH NO A GCLUINFIDH E SEO, BEATHA AGUS SLAINTE:

De bhrigh an ard-churaim ata curtha ormsa ag DAIL
EIREANN, ainmnighim trid seo

Art O Griobhtha, T.D., Aire um Ghnothai Coigcriche, Cathaoirleach.

Micheal O Coileain, T.D. Aire Airgid,

Riobard Bartun, T.D., Aire um Ghnothai Tionnscail,

Eamon O Dugain, T.D.,

Seoirse Gabhanach O Dubhthaigh, T.D.

mar Theachtai Lan-fheidhme o Riaghaltas Toghtha SAORSTAIT EIREANN
chum a dheanamh agus a thabhairt chum criche ar son na hEireann
le n-a Shoillse, SEOIRSE V. na Breataine, Connradh no Connartha
Socruighthe, Comh-bhainte agus Comh-oireamhna idir Eire agus an
saor-chumann naisiun ar a nglaodhtar Impreacht Shasana.

DA CHOMHARTHA SAN ag seo mo shighin mar Uachtaran.

I gCathair Bhaile Atha Cliath dhom
an 7 adh. la de Deire Foghmhair i
mbliain d'aois ar dTighearna 1921
agus deanta i gcuig macasamhla
bunusacha.

Eamon de Valera

3- R.B

'The M.F. [Michael Collins] told us that there was a general desire amongst the members of the Delegation that I should hold myself in readiness to go to London. You understand fully the considerations of tactical advantage which determined me in holding the view that I should remain here. If any new considerations arise it would be well that we should know them exactly so that we may weigh them all and if possible secure unanimity for whatever action is taken. My own position is that I am loathe to go unless the situation imperatively calls for it, and I am keeping an open mind.'

Éamon de Valera to Arthur Griffith, 25 October 1921
(NAI DE 2/304/1/5)

Abdruck unentgeltlich   Berlin, den 12. Oktober 1921

Irisches Bulletin Nr. 46

(Deutsches Büro für Nachrichten aus Irland, Berlin-Wilmersdorf, Nassauische Straße 4.)

Britischer Militarismus.

Ein Versuch, die Aussichten auf einen Erfolg der irischen Konferenz zu vereiteln.

Um die künftigen Beziehungen zwischen England und Irland festzusetzen, wurde gestern die Konferenz in London eröffnet. Vor ungefähr einer Woche schon sind anscheinend organisierte Angriffe von englischen Soldaten auf die Zivilbevölkerung in verschiedenen Teilen Irlands unternommen worden. Der gleichzeitige Ausbruch dieser Angriffe läßt darauf schließen, daß sie in der Absicht unternommen wurden, entweder die Bevölkerung zu Vergeltungsmaßregeln herauszufordern, oder die republikanische Armee wieder unter die Waffen zu rufen. In jedem dieser Fälle wurde den englischen Truppen Gelegenheit geboten, die Feindseligkeiten in großem Umfange wieder aufzunehmen, und unter solchen Umständen wurde eine Fortsetzung der Konferenz unmöglich gemacht. Durch seine Selbstkontrolle und Disziplin hat das irische Volk jedoch diese Versuche wenigstens für den Augenblick zunichte gemacht.

Auf die Größe der Herausforderung lassen die folgenden Einzelheiten schließen: Am 28. September wurde in den Straßen von Tipperary ohne jede vorhergehende Warnung von Soldaten der berüchtigten Hilfstruppen gefeuert. Von den Leuten, die gerade zu dieser Zeit aus einem Kino kamen, wurde ein Mann getötet und drei andere Personen, unter ihnen ein junges Mädchen, schwer verwundet.

Während eines Tanzabends, der in Galway am 2. Oktober veranstaltet war, griffen die Hilfstruppen junge Leute an, die im Begriff waren, in den Ballsaal zu gehen. Sie wurden durchsucht und verprügelt; dann stürmten die Soldaten in den Saal und schossen aus ihren Revolvern. Um dem Kugelregen zu entgehen, mußten sich die Tanzenden auf den Fußboden werfen. Eine Anzahl junger Mädchen wurde ohnmächtig, während alle anwesenden Männer in brutaler Weise durchsucht und mißhandelt wurden.

Am frühen Morgen des 6. Oktober erzwangen sich Soldaten den Eintritt in verschiedene Häuser der Stadt Thurles; sie schleiften die Schlafenden aus ihren Betten und schlugen so unbarmherzig auf sie ein, daß viele von ihnen infolgedessen ins Krankenhaus gebracht werden mußten. Nachdem sie ihren rohen Gelüsten genügend gefrönt hatten, verbrannten die Soldaten die Kleider und das Hausgerät ihrer Opfer.

An demselben Tage wurde in Cork ein junger Sinnfeiner auf offener Landstraße angehalten und erschossen.

Am 5. Oktober wurde ein Versuch gemacht, einen jungen Freiwilligen in Ballina zu erschießen, es gelang ihm jedoch zu entkommen.

In Dunmanway erschienen Hilfstruppen, feuerten nach allen Richtungen durch die Straßen und mißhandelten besonders alle diejenigen, die für ihre Sympathien mit den Sinnfeinern bekannt waren.

Wenn man die Tatsache in Betracht zieht, daß die oben erwähnten Städte verhältnismäßig weit von einander entfernt liegen, so muß man unbedingt zu dem Schluß kommen, daß diese Angriffe planmäßig und in der Absicht stattgefunden haben, das Volk zur Wiederaufnahme der Feindseligkeiten zu veranlassen, während die Konferenz tagt.

Die irischen Vertreter auf der Londoner Konferenz.

Arthur Griffith. Der Führer der irischen Delegation und der Vizepräsident der irischen Republik ist der Begründer der Sinnfein-Politik. Vor 20 Jahren fing er an zu predigen, daß Irland seine Rettung in sich selbst suchen müsse, anstatt sich auf fremde Hilfe zu verlassen oder auf die Zeit zu warten, in der England von Neue ergriffen werden könnte. Er lehrte, daß Irland seine eigenen Hilfsquellen entwickeln, seinen eigenen Handel aufrecht erhalten, seine eigene Sprache sprechen, seine eigene Musik und Kunst, seine eigenen Spiele und Tänze pflegen müsse, falls es dem Prozeß der Anglifizierung erfolgreichen Widerstand leisten wolle. Vor allem drang er darauf, daß die irischen Vertreter nicht länger nach Westminster gehen sollten, wo ihre Gegenwart eine stillschweigende Anerkennung des englischen Rechtes wäre, Irland Gesetze vorzuschreiben. Er hatte große Schwierigkeiten zu überwinden, um das irische Volk zur Annahme dieser letzterwähnten Theorie zu bewegen, aber dank seiner Beharrlichkeit gelangte er zum Ziel. Nach langen Jahren angestrengten Predigens in der Wüste bedeutet diese Konferenz einen großen Triumph für ihn.

Michael Collins war früher Generaladjutant der irischen republikanischen Armee und ist jetzt der Finanzminister der irischen Republik. Vor einigen Monaten setzte die englische Regierung einen Preis von tausend Pfund Sterling für Auskunft aus, die zu seiner Verhaftung führen würde. Jetzt ist es dem englischen Erstminister sehr angenehm, ihm auf dieser Konferenz zu begegnen.

Robert Barton verbüßte vor wenigen Monaten sein Urteil in einem englischen Gefängnis unter den niedrigsten englischen Verbrechern. Er wird von den Engländern besonders gehaßt, weil er seiner Geburt und Erziehung nach zu jener Klasse gehörte, die als „Englands treue Garnison in Irland" bekannt ist. Trotzdem wandte er sich von England ab und widmete sich ganz der irischen Bewegung.

Eamonn Duggan ist ein Jurist in Dublin. Im Juni unterzeichnete er die Waffenstillstandsbedingungen für die irische Armee, während General Macready für England zeichnete.

George Gavan Duffy war früher der irische Vertreter in Paris. Vor einem Jahre mußte er jedoch Paris verlassen auf Wunsch der französischen Regierung, die zu diesem Schritte durch Lord Derby, den damaligen englischen Gesandten in Paris, gezwungen wurde. Seitdem ist er der Vertreter Irlands in Rom.

Bemerkung. Ein unverkennbarer Fehler hat im letzten irischen Bulletin (Nr. 45) stattgefunden. Der Satz, der in der fünften Zeile der zweiten Spalte beginnt, sollte lauten: „Wir sind überzeugt, daß von dem Ergebnis der kommenden Verhandlungen der Erfolg oder der Mißerfolg der Konferenz in Washington abhängen wird."

German edition of the Dáil's propaganda newsletter, the *Irish Bulletin*, dated 12 October 1921, reporting on the Irish delegation's arrival in London. The Dáil had representatives in Berlin from April 1921 onwards.

NAI DFA/ES/1/9/64

The journey to London

The Irish delegation began its journey to London on the morning of Saturday 8 October 1921.

At 8.25am the main party of the delegation travelled in a special saloon carriage from Westland Row station to Dún Laoghaire (formerly Kingstown). They were cheered as the train left the platform by crowds who had gathered at the station.

Crowds waving tricolours also cheered the train along its route. The train terminated at Carlisle Pier and it was a short walk to board the steamer *Curraghmore* for the 100-kilometre passage across the Irish Sea to Holyhead. Police marshalled the orderly crowd who were waiting in expectation for a sight of Michael Collins, but he and the remaining members of the delegation travelled to London separately soon after the others.

From Holyhead the delegates departed by rail at 12.13pm on the *Irish Mail*, a fast express to Euston Station. Arriving in London at 5.40pm on the evening of 8 October, they were met by bands of Irish pipers to the air of 'The Jackets Green'. They were greeted by senior figures in the Irish Self-Determination League of Great Britain (ISDL) including its leader Art O'Brien, along with representatives from Sinn Féin, Cumann na mBan and the GAA.

King George V had arrived by train at Euston half an hour before the Irish delegates drew in. He got a share of the fervour of the crowds awaiting the delegation, estimated at 10,000.

The crowds watched as Arthur Griffith and his colleagues boarded a convoy of five cars for the eight-kilometre drive through London at dusk to the delegation's headquarters. 22 Hans Place, a narrow five-storey red sandstone townhouse in Knightsbridge would be their base for the next seven weeks.

Typescript note dated 8 October 1921 and initialed by 'MOC' [Míceál O'Coilean (sic); Michael Collins] in which he requests £50 to cover expenses as he prepared to depart for London. 'It would be serious if I could not give a porter a tip at Holyhead.'

NAI DE/5/2/35

Four of the five plenipotentiaries onboard the steamer *Curraghmore* at Dún Laoghaire Harbour on 8 October 1921, immediately prior to their departure. Left to right: Robert Barton, Arthur Griffith, Éamonn Duggan, George Gavan Duffy. The fifth plenipotentiary, Michael Collins, travelled to London the following day.

Courtesy of the National Library Ireland. INDH94

Dáil Éireann.

<table>
<tr><td>Aireact Airgid
Át-Cliat.</td><td>Department of Finance.
DUBLIN.</td></tr>
</table>

8. 10. 1921.

I don't know at the moment whether there is a special financial arrangement made for the remainder of the party. Please send me £50 which I'll account for separately. It can be incorporated in the general accounts later on. At the moment I have about £3 in my pocket. It would be serious if I could not give a porter a tip at Holyhead.

MOC

G.M.

Sent £50.
d.od.
8/x/21

£15 send

Members of the delegation on the deck of the *Curraghmore*. Left to right: Ellie Lyons, Alice Lyons, Arthur Griffith, Kathleen McKenna.

Courtesy of the National Library Ireland. MKN32

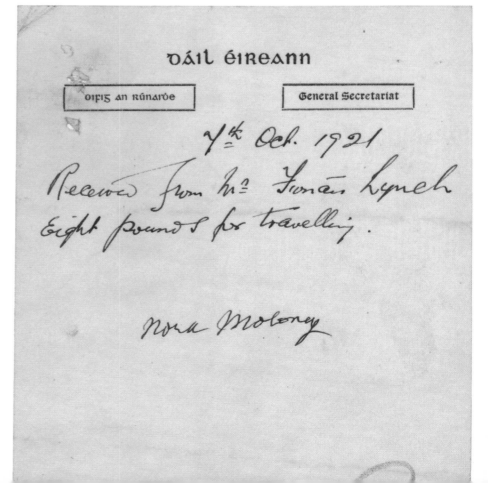

Received from Mr. F. Lynch, T.D. the sum of £2-1-8 in respect of portage of luggage, gratuities etc, in connection with the journey from Dublin to London.

Signed _[signature]_

Dated 8th October, 1921.

Thursday Oct 6th 1921.

J Kavanagh		5 fares Dublin to London.	£ 12 " 8 " 9
E O'Brien } Waiters		car fares in Dublin	£ 1 " 2 - 6
J O'Brien		refreshment on Boat & Train	2 " 4 " 6
		7 Oct 1921. Taxi fare to Hotel	7 - 6
S. Downing		Taxi fares	15 - 6
A. McCormack } Maids		Breakfast	15 " 3
		expenses on Boat & Train	16 " 0
		Trades men	15 " 0
		9th Oct 1921	
		Taxi to Jermyn Ct. Hotel	5 " 0
		10th Oct. 1921.	
		Trades men	6 " 0
		1 Bottle Brandy	£1 - 4 - 0
		Telegram to Col. Gr.	1 " 9
		Trades man	3 " 0
		Taxis .	5 " 0
			£ 21 " 12 " 9

Travelling 19 - 0 = 18 - 15 - 9
Tips Household 2 - 17
Brandy WO 1 - 8 - 0

(16)

Notes of travel expenses submitted by members of the Irish delegation.

NAI DE/3/1/15, 16, 17

Arthur Griffith poses for the press on board *Curraghmore* as it steams out of Dublin Bay, 8 October 1921.

Courtesy of the National Library of Ireland. INDH382

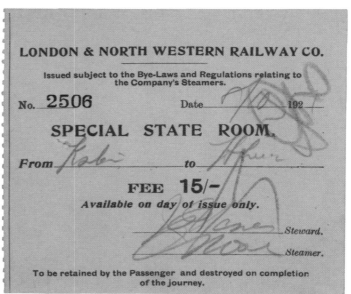

LONDON & NORTH WESTERN RAILWAY CO.

Issued subject to the Bye-Laws and Regulations relating to the Company's Steamers.

No. 2506   Date_____192_

SPECIAL STATE ROOM.

From_____ to_____

FEE 15/-
Available on day of issue only.

_____Steward.

_____Steamer.

To be retained by the Passenger and destroyed on completion of the journey.

Ticket for the Irish Sea crossing purchased for the delegation's journey to London, 8 October 1921.

NAI/3/1/1/14

A receipt for refreshments purchased by the delegation on the *Curraghmore*, 8 October 1921.

NAI DE/3/1/18

A note from Michael Collins to Éamon de Valera, dated 9 October 1921. 'Am writing this just prior to departure and I have a sad heart.'

Courtesy of UCD Archives P150/1377

It is particularly requested that no money be paid without a bill.

(1789) London & North Western Rly.

S.S. _School_
8 Oct 21 19

	£	s.	d.
BREAKFAST—			
LUNCHEON—			
TEA—		1/	
DINNER—			
SUPPER—			
BLACK COFFEE—			
SUNDRIES—			
WINES &c.			
TOTAL £		1/	

No. 165296

Óglaiġ na h-Éireann.

Árd-Oifiġ, Áṫ Cliaṫ.

General Headquarters,
Dublin.

Department..................
Reference No................

9 / 10 / 1921.

My Dear de V.

I think there is a very good suggestion
in the attached — the idea that you should have a
Presidential statement in Tuesday's papers regarding
the Delegates.   Am writing this just prior to
departure and I have a sad heart.

Yours sincerely,

Mícheál

An undated typescript list of members of the Irish delegation in London. Only four of the plenipotentiaries are listed; George Gavan Duffy's name is omitted. Éamonn Duggan and Fionán Lynch are listed by the English versions of their forenames: 'Edmond' (sic) and 'Finian' respectively.

NAI DE/3/7/1

Dáil Éireann.

Torcaireact Feadmannac na hÉireann.

Oifig an Rúnaide.

IRISH DELEGATION OF PLENIPOTENTIARIES.

SECRETARIAT.

DELEGATION

(Mr.Arthur Griffith,
(Mr.Michael Collins,
(Mr.Robert Barton,
(Mr.Edmond Duggan.

STAFF

Mr.Erskine Childers,
Mr.Finian Lynch,
Mr.Dermot O'Hegarty,
Mr.Daniel McCarthy,
Mr.Michael Knightley,
Mr.Sean Milroy,
Mr.Diarmaid Fawsitt,
Mr.L.Smith-Gordon,
Mr.David Robinson,
Mr.Desmond FitzGerald,
Professor Smiddy,
      "   Oldham,
Mr.J.J.Murphy,
Mr.Henry Mangan,
Mr.Joseph McGrath,
Mr.Edward Troy,
Mr.Joseph Foran,
Mr.Joseph Gill,
Mr.John McBride,
Mr.Wm. Morgan,
Mr.E.Dalton,
Mr.J.J.O'Connell,
Miss L.O'Brennan,
Miss McKenna,
Miss E.Lyons,
Miss A.Lyons,
Miss Conry,
Mrs.Duggan.

Oáil Éijeann.

Corcaijeact Feadmannac na héijeann.

Oifig an Rúnaide,

IRISH DELEGATION OF PLENIPOTENTIARIES.

SECRETARIAT.

STAFF - HOUSE.

Miss O'Donohoe,
Miss Flynn,
Miss Maloney,

Miss Healon,
Miss Foey,
Miss McCormick,
Miss Dowling

Mr. Thomas Kavanagh,
Mr. E. O'Brien,

Mr. J. O'Brien,
Mr. Michael Markey,

Settling in

The members of the Irish delegation were in the public eye as soon as they alighted from the ferry at Holyhead.

In London the delegation was based in two townhouses: 22 Hans Place in Knightsbridge and 15 Cadogan Gardens in nearby Chelsea. The Irish delegates would eat, sleep and work at these addresses and were wary of accepting any official hospitality from the British government.

They had a serious task ahead of them. 22 Hans Place became their headquarters and was transformed into a working overseas mission. Most of the delegation stayed there, though Michael Collins stayed at Cadogan Gardens, from where he also fulfilled his role as IRA director of intelligence. Much of the secretarial work was carried out at Cadogan Gardens. Arthur Griffith noted that the two townhouses were not large enough to cater for everyone present and that some of the delegation were staying in hotels nearby. Limousines were rented for transporting the plenipotentiaries, while an aircraft was purchased to allow for a quick getaway should negotiations break down.

The Irish delegation was welcomed by some and met hostility from others. When the plenipotentiaries arrived at Downing Street for the first time on 11 October they were met by crowds of well-wishers from London's Irish community. Two nights before, the footpath outside 22 Hans Place had been painted with the word 'murderers'.

The negotiations were covered extensively in the press. Collins and the delegation secretaries became particular subjects of fascination. The Irish offices at Hans Place and Cadogan Gardens were a magnet for journalists and visitors, including literary luminaries such as George Bernard Shaw and Ezra Pound. Members of the IRA passed through the offices occasionally while seeking to obtain weapons in London in case the truce broke down and hostilities resumed.

Invoice for the hire of various household items for the Irish delegation, dated 7 October 1921 and addressed to Art O'Brien.

NAI DE/3/1/1/4

MAYFAIR CATERING Co. LTD.,

SOCIETY BALL FURNISHERS.

Telephone,
MAYFAIR 175:

Telegraphic Address: "RIAFYAM", AUDLEY, London.

34, NORTH ROW,
GROSVENOR SQUARE,

LONDON, W.1.

Brien Esq.,
(per I. I. Hennessy Esq.)
ames' Place,
SW 1.

October 7 1921.

(4)

at 15 Cadogan Gardens

To furnishing on hire for
period of One month (4 weeks)
fine Silver Plate, Cutlery & Glass
for House Party, and other goods
for Staff use, according to list
supplied, and esteemed order
for sum of Forty pounds   £ 40 0 0

Received cheque £40.
With thanks
Mayfair Catering Co Ltd
J. L.
8/10/21.

ROLLS-ROYCE & OTHER HIGH-CLASS CARS FOR HIRE.
CARS BOUGHT AND SOLD ON COMMISSION.
MOTOR DRIVING TAUGHT.

PAVILION GARAGE CO.,
PAVILION ROAD, SLOANE SQUARE, S.W 1.

PETROL, TYRES, OILS,
GREASE, &c., STOCKED. MECHANICAL
REPAIRS AND CARRIAGE WORK OF EVERY DESCRIPTION.

Manager : W. E. BURKIN.

TELEPHONES: { VICTORIA 4295.
KENSINGTON 2367.

TELEGRAMS: "BYROAD." SLOANE. LONDON.

London, October. 15 th. 1921

1921   L. FO. 320.

Oct 7 th.	To Hire of Rolls Royce Cars.				
	R. 526. From 10. am to 11.45 pm.	£	7	7	-
8 th.	L.D. 3409. " 5.15 pm to 8.30 pm.		1	1	-
"	X.F. 7333. " " " " 12.10 am.		7	7	-
"	X.F. 6824. " " " " 8. pm.		1	1	-
"	B.H. 6434. " " " " 7.45 pm.		1	1	-
"	C.D. 676 " " " " 7.45 pm.		1	1	-
"	Van. " 5. pm to 7.20 pm.		1	10	-
"	R.526 " 10 am to 10 pm. £6.10. - 10 pm to 4 am.		9	13	-
	£3. 3.				
9 th.	R. 536. " 9.30 am to 11.50 pm.		7	7	-
"	L.P. 5364. " 10. am to 10 pm. £6.10. 10 pm to 8. am		13	-	-
	£6.10.				
	Carried Forward.	£	50	8	-

Invoice addressed to Art O'Brien via 22 Hans Place for the hire of cars, mostly Rolls-Royces, for the use of the Irish delegation. Rolls-Royces had been hired from the same garage in July 1921 for the delegation led by Éamon de Valera.

NAI DE/3/1/1/12

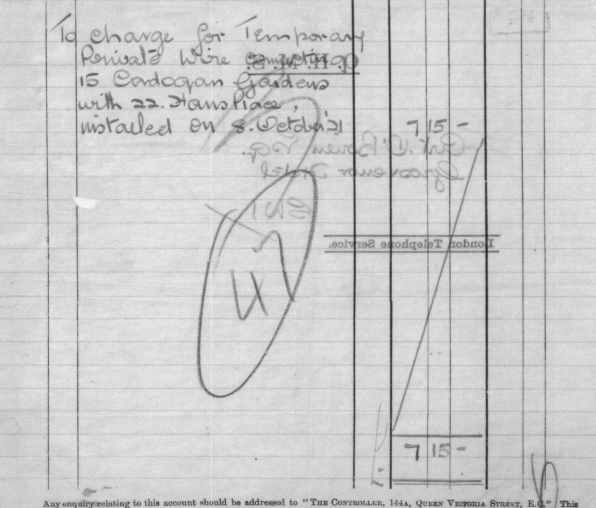

L.T.S. 108 N.

LONDON TELEPHONE SERVICE.

144A, QUEEN VICTORIA STREET, E.C. 4

15. October 1921

TELEGRAPHIC ADDRESS:
"PHONES. CENT, LONDON."

TELEPHONE NUMBER: CITY 2000.
(PRIVATE BRANCH EXCHANGE.)

AR3E

Exchange..... Private Wire

Number..... N⁰/25

Memorandum of amount due to the Postmaster-General on Telephone Account.

Remittances or enquiries should be accompanied by this form.

To charge for Temporary
Private Wire connecting
15 Cadogan Gardens
with 22. Hans Place,
installed on 8. October '21   7 15 -

7 15 -

Any enquiry relating to this account should be addressed to "THE CONTROLLER, 144A, QUEEN VICTORIA STREET, E.C." This account may be paid at the Controller's Office or at any Post Office. This form should be produced, and in no case will payment be accepted at a Post Office unless this condition is fulfilled and the full amount tendered. Cheques, etc., should be made payable to "The Postmaster General or Bearer," and be crossed a/c "H.M. Postmaster General."

Invoice dated 15 October 1921 for the installation of a
temporary private telephone line connecting the Irish
delegation's offices at 15 Cadogan Gardens and 22 Hans Place.

NAI DE/3/1/1/47

'Night had closed in and London had decked herself with lights when we passed through the heart of it on our way back to Hans Place where supper awaited us'.

Kathleen Napoli-McKenna,
A Dáil girl's revolutionary recollections (Dublin, 2014)

Members of the secretariat making their way to 15 Cadogan Gardens. Left to right: Alice Lyons, Kathleen McKenna and Ellie Lyons.

Courtesy of the Military Archives, Dublin

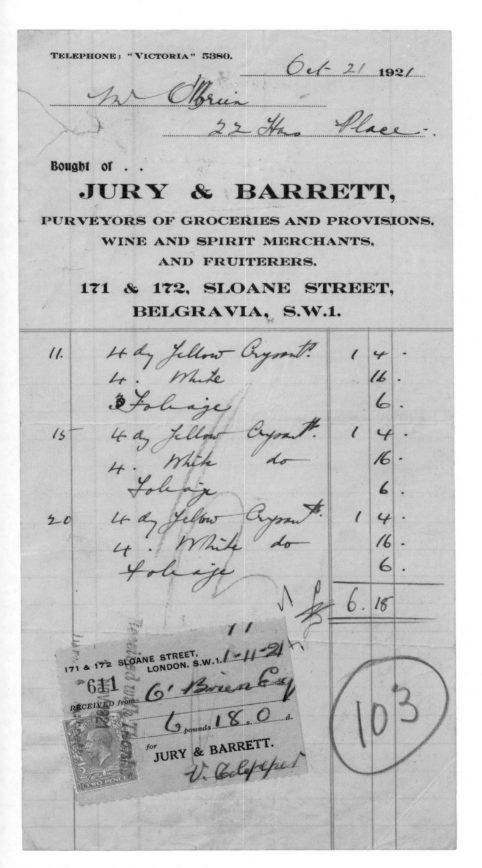

TELEPHONE: "VICTORIA" 5380.

Oct 21 1921

Mr O'Brien

22 Hans Place.

Bought of . .

JURY & BARRETT,

PURVEYORS OF GROCERIES AND PROVISIONS.
WINE AND SPIRIT MERCHANTS,
AND FRUITERERS.

171 & 172, SLOANE STREET,
BELGRAVIA, S.W.1.

11.	4 dz Yellow Chrysant.ᵗ	1	4	.
	4 . White		16	.
	3 Foliage		6	.
15	4 dz Yellow Chrysant.ᵗ	1	4	.
	4 . White do		16	.
	Foliage		6	.
20	4 dz Yellow Chrysant.ᵗ	1	4	.
	4 . White do		16	.
	Foliage		6	.
		£ 6	18	

171 & 172 SLOANE STREET,
LONDON, S.W.1. 1-11-21

£1ⁱ⁵⁹

RECEIVED from.. O'Brien Esq

6 pounds 18 0 s. d.

for JURY & BARRETT.

V. Colepepet

103

Receipt for everyday items and services
requested by the Irish delegation.

NAI DE/3/1/103

67

PARTICULARS OF EXPENSES TO LONDON.

			£	s.	d.
16th October.	Taxi Gresham Hotel, Mansion House and Westland Row.		£0.	10.	
" "	Return Ticket (first class).		8.	2.	8.
" "	Bed on train (two).		1.	10.	
17th "	Taxi Euston - Hans Place.			10.	
" "	Taxi Grosvenor Hotel.			5.	
18th "	do.			5.	
" "	Bed(Grosvenor Hotel) one night.			12.	6.
" "	Taxi Grosvenor to Euston Station.			10.	
19th "	Breakfast, dinner & tea. train.		1.	10.	
" "	Taxi Westland Row - Mansion House and President.			10.	
	Total		£14.	5.	2.

Received £ 14: 5" 2.

Enuo Duffy

1/11/31

99

A photograph captioned 'Sinn Féin delegates in conference at their London headquarters', originally published in the *Irish Independent*, 12 October 1921. Seated, left to right: Arthur Griffith, Éamonn Duggan, Michael Collins, Robert Barton. Standing, left to right: Erskine Childers, George Gavan Duffy and John Chartres.

Courtesy of the National Library of Ireland. POLF31

Typed list of expenses submitted by Eoin O'Duffy, the IRA's deputy chief of staff, for a return journey from Dublin to London, where he attended meetings on naval and air defence in October 1921. Such long and demanding journeys became a regular feature of life for the Irish negotiators.

NAI DE/3/1/1/99

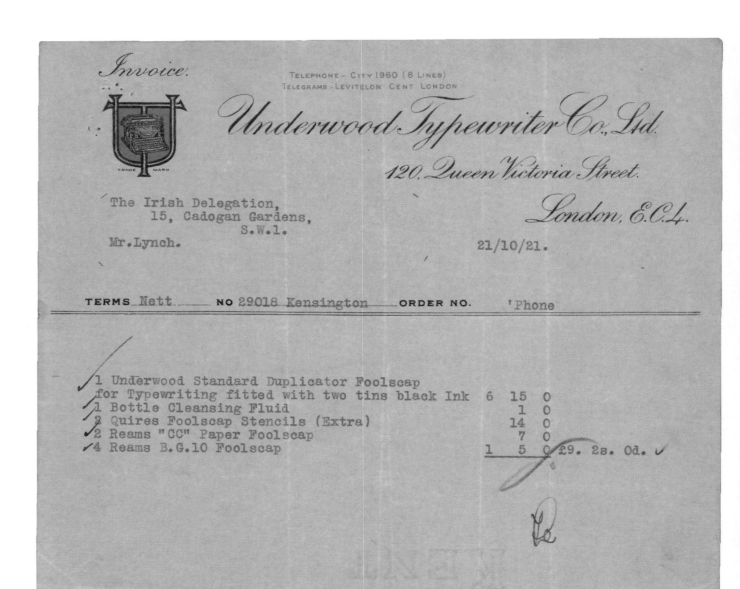

Invoice.

TELEPHONE - CITY 1960 (8 LINES)
TELEGRAMS - LEVITELON CENT LONDON

Underwood Typewriter Co., Ltd.

120, Queen Victoria Street.

London, E.C.4.

The Irish Delegation,
    15, Cadogan Gardens,
        S.W.1.
Mr.Lynch.

21/10/21.

TERMS Nett   NO 29018 Kensington   ORDER NO.   'Phone

1 Underwood Standard Duplicator Foolscap for Typewriting fitted with two tins black Ink	6	15	0	
1 Bottle Cleansing Fluid		1	0	
2 Quires Foolscap Stencils (Extra)		14	0	
2 Reams "CC" Paper Foolscap		7	0	
4 Reams B.G.10 Foolscap	1	5	0	£9. 2s. 0d.

An invoice for stationery and office equipment delivered to the Irish delegation's office at Cadogan Gardens.

NAI DE/3/1/163

Members of the Irish delegation in London,
10 October 1921. Left to right: Éamonn Duggan,
May Duggan, Arthur Griffith.

Courtesy of the National Library of Ireland. NPA MKN31

The Irish Self-Determination League of Great Britain (ISDL)

Irish nationalists and republicans traditionally drew support from the Irish diaspora worldwide.

The ISDL was founded in Manchester in 1919. The driving force behind it was the London-born activist Art O'Brien, who had been appointed as the Dáil's official emissary in Britain in January 1919. The ISDL drew most of its membership from Irish communities in London and the industrial heartlands of the north of England, raising funds for Dáil Éireann and organising propaganda in support of Irish independence and in opposition to British policy in Ireland. O'Brien assisted in securing accommodation for the Irish delegation in London, and the ISDL arranged a huge reception for the Irish delegation at London's Royal Albert Hall on 26 October 1921.

Letter from a Welsh branch of the Irish Self-Determination League of Great Britain (ISDL) dated 12 October 1921, pledging support for the Irish delegation soon after its arrival in London.

NAI DE/ES/1/4

J. WALSH,
Hon. Secretary.

36, Clarence Street,

Newport, Mon.,

Oct 12ᵗʰ 1921

A. Chara

I am directed by members of the about to submit the following resolution. (That we the members of the Newport Branch of the I. S. D. L. place our entire Conferdence in the Irish Peace Delegates of whom we hold are the right and proper persons to dicide the future wellfare of Ireland and we pledge them our united support in whatever action they may think fit to take.) Trusting that the time is not distant when the Oppresions of seven & a half centuries will be rewarded with an United Irish Republic.. I remain

Is misa do Chara

J. Walsh

Hon. Sec

The Treaty negotiations

The negotiations began at 11.00am on 11 October at 10 Downing Street.

The British side had resolved to establish a cordial atmosphere from the outset, and Prime Minister Lloyd George greeted the Irish negotiators with a handshake. The talks would last for seven weeks. Formal negotiations and more informal discussions took place between 11 October and 6 December in a variety of locations: 10 Downing Street, the prime minister's country residence at Chequers, the Grosvenor Hotel, offices in the Palace of Westminster, the Irish offices at Hans Place and even the private residences of figures such as Winston Churchill. They concluded where they had begun, at 10 Downing Street.

Arthur Griffith arrives at Downing Street for the opening of the negotiations, 11 October 1921.

Courtesy of the National Library of Ireland. NPA MKN30

'The negotiations commenced at 10, Downing St., the official residence of the British Prime Minister, on the morning of Tuesday, 11th October. About a dozen of us accompanied the Irish Delegation in Rolls Royce cars as far as No. 10. Amongst us were Liam Tobin, our assistant Director of Intelligence, Captain Robinson and Tom Barry of Cork, who was there on his own demand.

Some of the mass of pressmen present saw, or thought they saw, the outline of revolvers in some of our pockets, and duly published the fact. A good deal of fuss was made about this incident.

At the Cenotaph immediately outside a wreath had been specially placed that day *"In memory of the 586 members of His Majesty's naval, military and police forces murdered in Ireland".*'

Éamon Broy, who acted as 'escort and private secretary'
to Michael Collins in London, recalls the first arrival
of the Irish delegation at Downing Street
(Military Archives, Dublin, BMH WS 1280)

Members of the secretariat working in Hans Place. Left to right: Ellie Lyons, Kathleen McKenna, Alice Lyons. .

Courtesy of Mercier Archive. MAPress2

A stylised depiction of the negotiations in progress in the Cabinet room of 10 Downing Street, originally published in the *Illustrated London News*, 5 November 1921.

NAI PRIV/1093/16/1

'Erskine Childers, will have notified you about things yesterday – I never felt so relieved at the end of any day, and I need hardly say I am not looking forward with any pleasure to resumptions – such a crowd I never met… This place [the] bloody limit. I wish to God I were back home.'

Michael Collins to Éamon de Valera, 12 October 1921
(UCD Archives P150/1929)

Michael Collins pictured on the balcony of 22 Hans Place, October 1921.

Courtesy of the National Library of Ireland. POLF30

The British delegation

The Irish negotiators faced a formidable British delegation. The plenipotentiaries lacked the political and diplomatic experience of their British counterparts, many of whom had recently been involved in negotiating the post-First World War peace treaties.

To be assured of having a balanced team, Lloyd George drew from both parties in his Liberal-Conservative coalition government.

The British negotiators were supported by able civil servants, especially Lionel Curtis and Thomas Jones, the deputy secretary to the British Cabinet. Jones became a crucial intermediary whose actions on occasion brought the talks back from the brink of collapse.

Senior members of the British coalition government at an unidentified location soon after the December 1918 general election. Most of those pictured were members of the British delegation during the Treaty negotiations. From left to right: Sir Laming Worthington-Evans, Winston Churchill, Lord Birkenhead, David Lloyd George, Austen Chamberlain. Also pictured is George Nathanial Curzon, Marquess Curzon of Kedleston, secretary of state for foreign affairs.

Private collection

Three of the British negotiators emerging from 10 Downing Street during the Treaty negotiations. From left to right: David Lloyd George, Lord Birkenhead, Winston Churchill.

Alamy

David Lloyd George

David Lloyd George (1863–1945) was born in Manchester to Welsh parents. His family returned to Wales and he became a solicitor on leaving school. Becoming active in Welsh politics, he was elected Liberal MP for Caernarvon Boroughs in 1890. He retained the seat until his death.

Lloyd George was socially progressive, independent minded and ruthlessly ambitious. He was an exceptionally skillful and charismatic politician and his career flourished. In 1908 he was appointed chancellor of the exchequer.

During the First World War he served as minister of munitions and secretary of state for war. Becoming prime minister in December 1916, Lloyd George dominated the wartime and post-war Liberal-Conservative coalition governments he led.

Internationally he was instrumental in the negotiating of the post-war peace treaties.

Concerning Ireland, Lloyd George had overseen unsuccessful attempts to implement Home Rule after 1916. He took an uncompromising stance against Sinn Féin and the IRA for much of the War of Independence before accepting the necessity for a settlement. Lloyd George was the key figure among the British negotiators.

Frederick Edwin Smith, Lord Birkenhead

Frederick Edwin Smith, Lord Birkenhead (1872–1930) was born in Birkenhead, Cheshire. After attending Wadham College, Oxford, he embarked on a highly successful legal career. Elected Conservative MP for Liverpool Walton in 1906, he rose to prominence for his forensic attacks on the Liberal governments of Sir Henry Campbell-Bannerman and Herbert Asquith.

Smith was a staunch supporter of Ulster unionism during the Home Rule crisis of 1912–14 and an early advocate of partition. In 1915 he was appointed solicitor-general and subsequently attorney general. In this latter capacity he led the prosecution of Roger Casement for treason in 1916. He was appointed lord chancellor in January 1919 and conferred with the title of Lord Birkenhead the following month.

Trusted by Lloyd George, Birkenhead struck up a good rapport with the Irish delegation. His credentials as a Tory unionist helped to ensure that the hostility of many in the Conservative Party towards Irish republicans did not undermine the negotiations.

Joseph Austen Chamberlain

Joseph Austen Chamberlain (1863–1937) was born in Birmingham. He was the son of Liberal Unionist politician Joseph Chamberlain. Educated at Rugby School and Cambridge, he entered parliament in 1892 as Liberal Unionist (later Conservative) MP for East Worcestershire.

Chamberlain served as chancellor of the exchequer (1903–5). He later served as secretary of state for India (1915–17) in the wartime coalition government and was reappointed chancellor of the exchequer in the post-war coalition in January 1919.

In March 1921 Chamberlain became the leader of the Conservative Party in the House of Commons after party leader Andrew Bonar Law stepped down due to ill health. Chamberlain was now leader of the House of Commons and was also appointed lord privy seal.

Chamberlain's views on Ireland were more moderate than those of many in his party. He was a strong advocate of negotiating a settlement with Sinn Féin, and of the eventual Treaty.

Winston Churchill

Hamar Greenwood

Gordon Hewart

Winston Churchill (1874–1965), son of the Conservative politician Lord Randolph Churchill, was born at Blenheim Palace, Oxfordshire. Educated at Harrow School and the Royal Military Academy, Sandhurst, he was commissioned as a cavalry officer and developed a lucrative parallel career as a war correspondent.

In 1900 Churchill was elected to parliament as Conservative MP for Oldham. He defected to the Liberals in 1904, subsequently sitting as MP for North-West Manchester and later Dundee. He held a range of senior Cabinet posts in successive governments.

Churchill was appointed secretary of state for war and air in January 1919 and secretary of state for the colonies in February 1921. In both roles he played a major part in British policy towards Ireland.

Having advocated harsh measures in Ireland during the War of Independence, by May 1921 he supported opening negotiations and would establish good relationships with the Irish delegation. Churchill played a key role in the military and naval aspects of the Treaty negotiations.

Hamar Greenwood (1870–1948) was born in Ontario, Canada. He emigrated to England in 1895 to pursue a legal career and entered politics, being elected Liberal MP for York in 1906 and Sunderland in 1910. He saw service on the western front during the First World War before resuming his political career. He was appointed under-secretary for trade in January 1919 and became the last chief secretary for Ireland in April 1920.

As the British Cabinet minister responsible for Irish affairs, Greenwood supported the harsh policy that Lloyd George's government adopted towards the independence movement in Ireland. He became notorious for defending, indeed denying, the policy of official and unofficial reprisals carried out by British forces against civilians in Ireland during the War of Independence.

Greenwood was sidelined as Lloyd George moved towards negotiating with Sinn Féin in early 1921. He played a peripheral role in the Treaty negotiations.

Gordon Hewart (1870–1943) was born in Bury in Lancashire. Following a legal career he worked in journalism. Entering politics, he was elected Liberal MP for Leicester in 1913. Hewart was an 'advanced' Liberal, supporting causes including female suffrage and Home Rule for Ireland.

A skillful orator in court and in parliament, Hewart was appointed solicitor-general and knighted in 1916. Appointed attorney general in 1919, he declined various Cabinet posts, including that of chief secretary for Ireland, on the grounds that the attorney general would automatically be promoted to lord chief justice should a vacancy arise; this came to pass in 1921. As lord chief justice, the chief legal officer to the British government, Hewart was an essential member of the British delegation.

Laming Worthington-Evans

Laming Worthington-Evans (1868–1931) was born in Kent and educated at Eastbourne College. A solicitor, he was elected Conservative MP for Colchester in 1910, holding the seat for nineteen years.

Worthington-Evans held positions at the War Office in the early years of the First World War before moving to the Foreign Office. His career then accelerated. Created a baronet in 1916, he joined the Privy Council in 1918, became minister of pensions in January 1919 and minister without portfolio with a Cabinet seat in April 1920.

Worthington-Evans was by 1920 a trusted confidante of Lloyd George, and from early that year was heavily involved in the post-war peace conference, especially in the negotiations about Germany's war reparations. He was appointed secretary of state for war in February 1921, in which capacity he served as one of the British negotiators in the Treaty negotiations.

Lionel Curtis

Lionel Curtis (1872–1955) was born near Derby, Lancashire. He attended New College, Oxford, and fought in the Second Boer War (1899–1902) before becoming assistant secretary to Sir Alfred Milner, British high commissioner in South Africa.

In 1910 Curtis was a founding member of the broadly imperialistic 'Round Table' group and in 1912 became Beit Lecturer in Colonial History at the University of Oxford. His career as a colonial administrator led him to a new role as an intellectual advocate for maintaining the British Empire by allowing it to evolve into a federation or 'commonwealth' of self-governing 'dominions'.

In June 1921 Curtis publicly advocated that the 26 counties of 'Southern Ireland', as created by the Government of Ireland Act, 1920, should become a dominion. This, and his extensive imperial experience, saw him appointed one of the secretaries to the British delegation.

Thomas Jones

Thomas Jones (1870–1955) was born in Rhymni (Rhymney), Wales. Having originally studied for a Methodist ministry at the University College of Wales, he graduated with an economics degree from the University of Glasgow.

Jones worked as a visiting lecturer in Ireland (1904–5) and subsequently as a professor of political economy at Queen's University, Belfast (1909–10).

Following an early involvement with the Independent Labour Party and the moderately socialist Fabian Society, Jones moved to London in 1916 to work for Lloyd George. He served as both assistant and then deputy secretary to the Cabinet. Jones's brief was primarily domestic affairs. His experience and knowledge of Ireland, and his relationship with the prime minister (with whom he often conversed in Welsh) saw Jones appointed as one of the secretaries to the British delegation. In this capacity, he took part in both formal and informal negotiations with the Irish plenipotentiaries and became a crucial intermediary between the two sides.

The choreography
of the negotiations

The two sides met in plenary sessions until 24 October. After this the talks continued within sub-committees dealing with specific issues such as naval and air defence, financial arrangements and the maintenance of the truce. The British side split the Irish delegation and met them in various locations. They focused on their discussions with Griffith and Collins, who did most of the negotiating for the Irish side on the key issues.

The British side viewed Griffith and Collins as capable but were dismissive of other members of the Irish delegation. Lloyd George's strategy was to divide the inexperienced Irish negotiators, denying them the united Irish republic they sought but ensuring that the document eventually presented to them to sign contained as few offensive elements as possible. Both sides gave serious consideration to some of the issues that were of concern to each other.

The British negotiators had the advantage of being able to draw upon high-level civil-service support, and the talks were taking place on their own territory. The Irish delegation, on the other hand, was operating at a distance from home. The necessity for the plenipotentiaries to travel between London and Dublin to consult with the Dáil Cabinet became a gruelling obligation, given the length of the journey by rail and by sea. This ultimately led to tensions with de Valera and others in Dublin.

Letter dated 11 October 1921 from Arthur Griffith to Éamon de Valera giving his impressions of events after the initial meetings of the Irish and British delegations that day. Griffith noted that the question of the Crown and Ulster did not arise but predicted that 'When they do the sailing will be rough.'

NAI DE/2/304/1/10

Recd. 5 Fitzwm sqr.
11.15. am
Oct 12

rcaipeact feadmannaċ na hÉireann.

Oifig an Rúnaide.

2

IRISH DELEGATION OF PLENIPOTENTIARIES.

SECRETARIAT.

11. 10. 21.

A Ċara Coṁ

The meeting to-day has left on my mind the impression that the English Government is anxious for peace and also that this question of Naval defence re the coasts of Ireland is a fixed idea of theirs — that they believe it vital to their lives.

The question of the Crown and Ulster did not arise. When they do the sailing will be rough. To-day they were amiable and both sides were quite polite to each other. The report herewith abtɫ what occurred. But, of course, the discussion had very many points of interest, amusement, and instruction. Ll. G. is a remarkably suave and astute man, but on the whole, we have scored to-day although the most difficult part has yet to be discussed.

do cara (ɱ hata)

A. G.

Treaty oct /11

(1)

IRISH PEACE CONFERENCE.

The first meeting, October 11th, 1921, 11 a.m.

Present :-

1st Session

FOR ENGLAND :

> Mr. Lloyd George,
> Lord Birkenhead,
> Mr. Winston Churchill,
> Mr. J. Worthington Evans,
> Sir Hamar Greenwood,
> Sir Gordon Hewart —also attended .

> The Secretaries were Mr. Thomas Jones and
> Mr. Lionel Curtis.

FOR IRELAND :

> Mr. Arthur Griffith,
> Mr. Michael Collins,
> Mr. R.C. Barton,
> Mr. E.J. Duggan,
> Mr. G. Gavan Duffy,

> The Secretaries were Mr. Erskine Childers and
> Mr. John Chartres.

MR. LLOYD GEORGE — IN AN OPENING STATEMENT AFFIRMED THE DESIRE of England to make peace, but there were limitations beyond which he could not go. There were also limitations on the other side. If these limitations proved to be insuperable, then the responsibility for failure would rest not with those at the Council table but with others.

MR ARTHUR GRIFFITH — England's policy in the past had been to treat Ireland as a conquered and subject country. If there were a change in the policy of subordinating Ireland to English interests, then there appeared to be a possibility of peace.

MR. LLOYD GEORGE — The question of procedure was discussed and he invited objections to the proposals already made on behalf of England.

MR ARTHUR GRIFFITH — intimated that the six reservations made implied the military subordination of Ireland.

MR. LLOYD GEORGE — "We certainly don't desire that". They were not looking out for the military control of Ireland. He again repeated "We seek nothing in the way of military domination of Ireland".

Typescript copy of minutes: 'Irish Peace Conference.
The first meeting, October 11th 1921, 11 a.m.'

NAI DE2/304/1/13

MR LLOYD GEORGE   Referring to the Air question he said that Ireland was right in the track of communications, that naval Defence was largely a question of the Air, and that it was essential to have Aerodromes for purposes of naval defence in order to protect English merchant shipping against submarines.

Access to Irish ports by the English navy was necessary, not for commercial but for defence purposes - especially anti-submarine. "Our people might starve" - "purely defensive rights - not offensive in regard to yourselves".   He added "beyond these limitations we cannot go".   Coast defence was what they really cared about. "We are not thinking really of aerodromes except in so far as they are necessary for naval defence".

On this point he said that guarantees could be given, and in reply to a reference to 'broken treaties' in the past, said, " you have never made a Treaty with the people of this country before. Treaties in the past have been with oligarchies ruling this country.   This is your first chance of having a Treaty with the people".

Reference was made to the position of the Dominions in relation to defence and war, whereupon Mr Lloyd George said that Dominions' participation in war was their voluntary act and "so it will be with you".   "In war we hope for your support, but if you do not give it, well, it would not be worth asking for"
     (But see this afternoon's discussion. By "Support" he meant "resources".)

MR CHURCHILL   spoke of British rights at the Capetown naval port but admitted when questioned that the port was under S.African control.
     He consented to produce the papers about this

MR BARTON   said S.Africa need not join in a British war.

LORD BIRKENHEAD   "THat is not conceded".

The discussion turned on trade :

MR.LLOYD GEORGE   said that England was Ireland's only market and on the ground that England desired real peace strongly deprecated anything in the nature of tariff conflicts.   He referred to Austria's present condition as illustrating the disastrous consequences of such conflicts.

LORD BIRKENHEAD	said:"Nothing is intended to prevent the economic development of Ireland".
MR LLOYD GEORGE	Premiums and Bonuses and Bounties could be given. Ireland would be free to do anything to develop the country agriculturally and industrially. He reiterated that England was Ireland's sole market, whereas England could obtain her food stuffs from other countries. Tariff conflicts would be wars between the two peoples, the two democracies, and must result in trouble.
MR BARTON	"If we are dependent on you, why do you fear a tariff war ?"
MR. LLOYD GEORGE	"There is a temptation on both sides. I want peace".
MR BARTON	"We want to be self-supporting". Our independence in the past was always restricted by you.
MR LLOYD GEORGE	"We are not offering you 1779 terms."

ADJOURNMENT at 12.35 to 4 p.m.

SIGNED :   Arthur Griffith.

Hand-drawn plan, by Robert Barton, of the seating arrangements for the plenary conferences at 10 Downing Street.

NAI PRIV 1093/4/32

when Chamberlain was present he sat in Lloyd Georges R.

Greenwood

o Curtis

Evans

o Jones

Lloyd George

Churchill
Chamberlain

Birkenhead

Hewart

Duggan

o Chartres

Griffith

o Childers

Collins

Barton

Gavan Duffy

This is the way we sat at the Plenary Conferences at Downing St except the 1st & 2nd from which Chamberlain was absent.

Arthur Griffith and Michael Collins emerge from 10 Downing Street on 11 October 1921, the first day of the Treaty negotiations. On the far left is Emmet Dalton, who had served in the British Army during the First World War and subsequently joined the IRA; he organised the provision of an aircraft to fly Collins out of London should the talks break down.

On behalf of the IRA, Emmet Dalton arranged to purchase a Martynside A1 Mk. II biplane that could swiftly bring Collins and the other plenipotentiaries back to Ireland. It was kept in readiness in London, and the proposed landing place in Ireland was Leopardstown racecourse in south County Dublin. The aircraft was later used by the Irish Air Corps. Renamed *The Big Fella* in honour of Collins, in this image from February 1923 it is pictured at Air Corps Headquarters at Baldonnel Aerodrome, Dublin.

Courtesy of the Military Archives, Dublin

'P.S. Lloyd George is a humorous rascal. He talked today of the vast amount of produce England bought from us. I said "You don't buy it for love of our beautiful eyes" Whereupon, with a smile he yielded, saying "No, on account of your beautiful butter".'

Arthur Griffith to Éamon de Valera, 13 October 1921
(NAI DE 2/304/1)

Notes passed by Robert Barton to Michael Collins during
negotiations at 10 Downing Street, along with an unidentified sketch.

NAI PRIV 1093/4/1

we should have to recognise
ourselves as something different
from what we did coming here

It will be impossible for S.A.C.
to change anything. It ~~must~~
can only accept or reject
in toto

Detail from a 1920 Ordnance Survey map showing the Irish delegation's offices and the various locations in central London at which official negotiations and informal discussions took place between the British and Irish negotiators.

2 Sussex Square (Winston Churchill's house)

25 Park Lane (Sir Philip Sassoon's house)

10 Downing Street

Treasury

22 Hans Place

Grosvenor Hotel

15 Cadogan Gardens

Colonial Office

2 Whitehall Gardens

House of Lords

Dáil Éireann.

⁊

① Tocraiɼeaċt Feaḋmannaċ na hÉireann.

Oiɼiᵹ an Rúnaiḋe.

IRISH DELEGATION OF PLENIPOTENTIARIES.

SECRETARIAT.

24th October, 1921.

A Chara,

Miceal and I were asked to see Lloyd George and Chamberlain this evening at the conclusion of the Conference.

They talked freely -- Chamberlain frankly. The burden of their story was that on the Crown they must fight. It was the only link of Empire they possessed.

They pressed me to say that I would accept the Crown provided we came to other agreements. It was evident they wanted something to reassure themselves against the Die-Hards. I told them that I had no authority. If we came to an agreement on all other points I could recommend some form of association with the Crown. Conversation ranged over the document. They said it was impossible for them to accept our proposal re League of Nations and U.S.A. guaranteeing Ireland's freedom.

Question of elective Head arose. They shied at it. Wholly impossible to them.

Told them the only possibility of Ireland considering association of any kind with Crown was in exchange for essential unity -- a concession to Ulster.

Miceal got Chamberlain to admit that the general feeling in England was for a settlement. He countered their arguments on defence etc. all the time. But they always fell back on the impossibility of peace except on acceptance of Crown.

We agreed to proceed on basis of settling all other points, leaving Crown to last.

Meet again at 4 to-morrow.

Ⱥᵹⱬ Ó Ᵹríoḃṫa

Letter from Arthur Griffith to Éamon de Valera, dated 24 October 1921, recounting a private meeting held earlier between himself, Michael Collins, David Lloyd George and Austen Chamberlain. 'They talked freely – Chamberlain frankly. The burden of their story was that on the Crown they must fight'.

NAI DE/2/304/1/26

Dáil Éireann.

Toircaireact Feadmannac na hÉireann.

Oifig an Rúnaide.

9.

IRISH DELEGATION OF PLENIPOTENTIARIES.

SECRETARIAT.

October 26th, 1921.

A. E. A Chara,

Your letters reached me this evening.   It is impossible for me, with the engagements we have this evening and the time at my disposal to deal with all the matters.

I have got a meeting of the delegates and secretaries. The delegates regard the first paragraph of your letter No. 7 as tying their hands in discussion and as inconsistent with the powers given them on their appointment and Nos 1 and 2 of "Instructions to Plenipotentaries from Cabinet" dated 7th October.

Obviously any form of association necessitates discussion of recognition in some form or other of the <u>head</u> of the association.   Instruction 2 conferred this power of discussion but required before a decision was made reference to the members of the Cabinet in Dublin.

The powers were given by the Cabinet as a whole and can only be withdrawn or varied by the Cabinet as a whole.   Having regard to the stage discussions have reached now, it is obvious that we could not continue any longer in the Conference and should return to Dublin immediately *if the powers were withdrawn.* *A.G.*

We strongly resent, in the position in which we are placed, the interference with our powers.   The responsibility, if this interference breaks the very slight possibility there is, of settlement, will not and must not rest on the plenipotentiaries.

As to your coming to London, we think, if you can come without being known, it is most important you should do so immediately. *But if you cannt come privately do not come publicly unless we send you a message that in our opinion it is essential — A.G.*

Arz ú Ghobza

Riobárd Barún.

Seórfa Zabáin uí Durcaig

E.S. Ó Dugáin

Mícéál Ó Corcaig

Letter dated 26 October 1921 signed by all of the Irish plenipotentiaries and addressed to Éamon de Valera, in which they stated their opposition to what they felt was interference with their powers by de Valera. They also raise the question of whether de Valera should join the conference in London.

ROYAL ALBERT HALL

MANAGER .. .. HILTON CARTER, M.V.O.

Failtiugadh roimh teactairi Saorstait na hEireann o Cumman na hEireann agus muinntir na hEireann i gcomhnuidhe i Lunndain.

Reception of the Delegates of the Irish Republic by the Irish-Ireland Societies and Irish Residents of London.

WEDNESDAY, 26th OCTOBER, 1921.

AT **8** P.M. DOORS OPEN AT **7**.

SPECIAL PLATFORM

ENTER BY FRONT ENTRANCE

Invitation card to a reception in the Royal Albert Hall on 26 October 1921 held in honour of the Irish delegation. The ISDL was the main group involved in arranging this, along with other organisations such as the GAA. Press reports suggested that as many as 5,000 were in attendance.

Courtesy of the National Library of Ireland. MS 49, 835/10/1

Ticket stub for the reception held in the Royal Albert Hall on 26 October 1921.

Courtesy of the Military Archives, Dublin

The cover and central pages of the souvenir programme for the reception held in the Royal Albert Hall on 26 October 1921.

Courtesy of the Military Archives, Dublin

IE/AL/ISOL/13

SOUVENIR PROGRAMME

Reception to the
Irish Republican Delegation
By the Irish-Ireland Societies
In London.

Albert Hall,
Wednesday, 26th Oct., 1921.

CLÁR 1.

1 Organ .. .. Irish Airs
Mr. B. BARRETT

2 Píob Mór   Cumann na bPíobairí

3 Songs .. .. "An Cáilfíonn"
"She is far from the Land"
Miss AGNES TRACEY

4 Rince .. .. "Reel" "Jig"
THE CHILDREN OF THE FOREST GATE
SCHOOL OF THE GAELIC LEAGUE

5 Songs .. .. .. "Éamonn a'Cnuic"
"The West's Asleep"
Mr. PATRICK HENEBERY

ADDRESS OF WELCOME.

INTERVAL (20 mins).

CLÁR 2.

6 Songs .. "The Felons of our Land"
"Who fears to speak of '98?"
Mr. BERNARD DUDLEY

7 Violin .. .. Irish Airs
Misses EVALDA

8 Rince .. "Hornpipe" "Blackbird"
Messrs. O'BRIEN and FITZGERALD

9 Song .. .. Selected
Mr. JEROME MURPHY

10 Songs .. .. .. "Fuireógín Ruad"
"Rich and Rare"
Miss AGNES TRACEY

11 "THE SOLDIERS' SONG"

Accompanist: Miss AGNES McHALE.

A SILVER COLLECTION WILL BE MADE DURING THE INTERVAL.

CONFERENCE ON IRELAND

Memorandum of A Meeting at Mr Churchill's House at ten p.m. Sunday, October 30th, 1921.

Present:-

Mr Griffith   Mr Lloyd George
Mr Collins   Mr Churchill
                           Lord Birkenhead

Conversation between Mr Griffith and Mr Lloyd George.

Mr Lloyd George was anxious to know whether the Irish Memorandum of yesterday's date might be relied upon as a bona fide statement made in the interest of peace, and asked for further explanations. He said that three things were vital, namely, the Crown, the Empire and the Navy, and conversation ensued on these and other points.

The Crown. Mr Lloyd George asked for a personal assurance on this point. Mr Griffith gave him the assurance that we should be prepared to recommend a recognition of the Crown provided that we were satisfied on the other points at issue, and it was agreed that the formula in which this recognition was to be couched should be arrived at in discussion at a later stage.

The Empire. The formula defining the association of Ireland with the Empire was left over.

Naval and Air Defence. Mr Griffith pointed out that a new demand, namely that Ireland should have no Air Force, had been put forward in the last British document. Mr Lloyd George was understood to indicate that the point would not be pressed, at any rate as regards the military Air Force.
As regards the prohibition of an Irish Navy Mr Lloyd George said that this did not exclude revenue craft and gunboats, but he hoped it would exclude mine-layers. Mr Griffith suggested that there might be a time limit, say thirty years, and Mr Lloyd suggested that the prohibition should hold good until an agreement to the contrary was made.

Army. Mr Lloyd George suggested that the Irish military force should be limited to a size proportionate to population as compared with the British forces. Taking 400,000 as the British figure this would give Ireland 40,000 of which 10,000 would be allotted to Ulster. Mr Griffith said that in no circumstances could we agree to an Ulster army, whereupon Mr Lloyd George suggested a militia for Ulster. This point was left open.

Trade. Mr Lloyd George argued that a Convention as proposed in the Irish Memorandum was not possible as it could be broken off at any time. It was necessary to satisfy Ulster that its raw materials would not be taxed. Mr Griffith said that he did not wish at that time to deal with technicalities, but some agreement might be come to which would safeguard Ulster's industries.

Ulster. Mr Lloyd George said that he could carry a six-county Parliament subordinate to a national Parliament. Alternatively he said he would try to carry a plan for a new boundary or a vote on the inclusion or exclusion of the whole of Ulster as a unit, but he was not hopeful of doing so.

Note of a meeting between members of the two delegations in Winston Churchill's house on 30 October 1921.

NAI PRIV 1093/1/10

A memorandum noting various informal discussions between members of the two delegations and others, including southern unionist representatives, in November 1921. It is annotated by Éamon de Valera, though it is unclear whether his notes were contemporaneous or made later.

UCD Archives P150/1513

INFORMAL CONVERSATIONS.

No.	Date & Time	Place	Present	Remarks	Reference.
1. ✓	Novr 8th. 3 p.m.	Grosvenor Hotel	Mr.T.Jones Mr.M.Collins Mr.A.Griffith	Ulster	A.Griffith's letter to P. 8/11/21.
2. ✓	Novr 9th. evening	Grosvenor Hotel	T.Jones A.Griffith ~~Mr.Collins~~ E.J.Duggan	Ulster - full meeting of Brit.Cabinet to-morrow.	A.Griffith's letter to P. 9/11/21.
3. ✓	Novr 11th.	do.	T.Jones A.Griffith.	Ulster — Ulster Cabinets Reply.	A.Griffith's letter to P. 11/11/21.
4. ✓	Novr 12th a.m.	22, Hans Place	T.Jones A.Griffith	do.	A.Griffith's letter to P. 12/11/21. } sub-conference file
5. ✓	Novr 15th. 3 p.m.	do.	T.Jones A.Griffith	No record	
6. ✓	Novr 16th. a.m.	20, New Cavendish Street W.	A.Griffith Lord Midleton Dr.Bernard A.Jameson	Land Purchase Income tax Universities	A.Griffith's letter to P. 16/11/21. } sub-conference file

The Provost of Trinity College

INFORMAL CONVERSATIONS.

No.	Date & Time	Place	Present	Remarks	Reference
7 ✓	Novr 21st 8.30 p.m.	22, Hans Place	T.Jones ~~Mr.Collins~~ A.Griffith	No record.	
8. ✓	Novr 22nd 1.20 p.m.	do.	T.Jones M.Collins A.Griffith	Irish Memo of Nov 22nd.	A.Griffith's letter to P. 22/11/21.
9. ✓	Novr 30th 10 p.m.	do.	T.Jones A.Griffith M.Collins E.J.Duggan	T.Jones brought the Brit.Proposed Articles of Agreement	~~letter to P. from A.Griffith~~ no record.
10 ✓	Decr ~~4th~~ 4th. 5 3.a.m.	do.	T.Jones A.Griffith	Mr.L.George's request to see M.Collins	M.Collin's minute of Decr 5th.

Key issues

There were seven weeks of negotiations between the morning of 11 October and the early hours of 6 December 1921. The talks were as much about the future of the British Empire as they were about Ireland's future relationship with Britain.

The British side was intent on securing an agreement and had a clear sense of what they wanted to achieve. The most important issues for them were to maintain the integrity of the British Empire given the rise of independence movements in India and Egypt, and to preserve Britain's strategic military needs in Ireland. These related to naval control of the approaches to the Atlantic Ocean, especially in time of war. They were unwilling, in any circumstances, to accept the complete separation of Ireland from the Empire in the form of an independent Irish republic.

Despite the efforts of the Irish negotiators to secure concessions on Irish unity, the maintenance of Northern Ireland and therefore partition was a given as far as the British were concerned. The Ulster Unionist leader Sir James Craig, who had recently become the first prime minister of Northern Ireland, was unwilling to make any concessions to the prospect of Irish unity. Many in the Conservative Party were naturally sympathetic to Irish unionists and were instinctively hostile to Irish republicanism. Lloyd George and his colleagues were conscious that they faced pressure from their own supporters not to concede too much to Sinn Féin. The Irish negotiators recognised this reality; they were in a similar situation themselves.

For the Irish plenipotentiaries, sovereignty and Irish unity were the critical issues. The Dáil Cabinet had agreed to seek an outcome suggested by de Valera, in which Ireland would voluntarily align itself with the British Empire as an associate rather than a full member. This implicitly accepted that the Irish negotiators were not going to return from London with a fully independent republic. It was felt that this compromise might be acceptable at home if a united Ireland could be obtained; however, 'external association' and a definite ending of partition were both unacceptable to the British.

The British negotiators recognised that partition was the issue on which the Irish were likely to try to break off the negotiations with a view to appealing to Irish and international opinion, a scenario they wanted to avoid. During the negotiations Lloyd George proposed that a 'boundary commission' could determine the final border with Northern Ireland. This was later used to win Griffith over and thus avoid a breakdown in the talks over 'Ulster'. The British side was only prepared to break off the talks over the issue of an Irish refusal to formally remain within the British Empire. This nearly happened in the final days of the negotiations but was avoided.

A page from Robert Barton's annotated copy of Éamon de Valera's proposals for a settlement as discussed at a Cabinet meeting in Dublin on 7 October 1921, prior to the delegation's departure for London. It proposed that Ireland should be associated with the British Commonwealth rather than become a full member.

NAI PRIV 1093/4/51

DeValera's Outline of a Treaty.

Barton

Instructions to
Plenipotentiaries
from cabinet.

Before any big departure
communicate

1. Powers   In accordance
   with credentials.

2. It is understood that before
   decisions are finally
   reached on the main Qs.
   that a dispatch notifying
   the intention of making
   such decisions will be
   sent to the Cabinet in
   Dublin & a reply awaited
   before final decision is made.

3. also understood that
   the complete text of the
   draft Treaty about to be signed
   will be similarly submitted
   & reply awaited

4. In case of break the
   text of final proposals
   from our side will be
   similarly submitted.

5. It is understood that
   the Cabinet in Dublin will
   be kept regularly informed
   of the progress of negotiations

1. Invitation in forefront
   others drafted in by Britain
   or not by us (verbal by Dev.)

---

who signs on behalf & behalf of

The Government of Great Britain, the
Government of the Dominion of Canada, the
Government of the Commonwealth of Australia,
the Government of the Dominion of New Zealand,
the Government of the Union of South Africa,
and the Government of the Colony of Newfoundland
being separate members of the British Imperial *or such*
Conference and together constituting the group *of them*
of partner sovereign states known and in this *as consent*
Treaty referred to as the British Commonwealth *to sign*
this
treaty

and

The Elected Government of Ireland

having considered the invitation extended to
Ireland by Great Britain in the name of the
British Commonwealth to enter into free
association with the States constituting the
British Commonwealth, and having considered
the common desire of the British Commonwealth
and of Ireland to the ruinous secular conflict
between Great Britain and Ireland and to secure
the benefits of amity and concord

have resolved to conclude the following Treaty
of Settlement, Accommodation and Association,
and for that purpose have appointed

The British Commonwealth

---

and the Elected Government of Ireland

---

who, after communicating to each other their
respective full powers, found in good and due
form, have agreed upon the following articles:

ARTICLE I.

The British Commonwealth recognises
Ireland as a sovereign and independent State,
and Great Britain (relinquishes) all claims to
any interference in Ireland or in Irish
affairs, whether by way of government,
legislation, control, or otherwise.

✓
renounces.

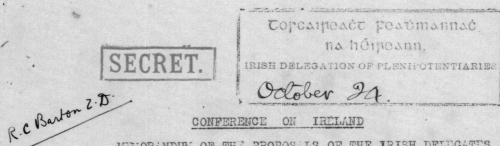

SECRET.

Torcaireact Feavmannac
na hÉireann.
IRISH DELEGATION OF PLENIPOTENTIARIES

October 24

R.C Barton Z.D

CONFERENCE ON IRELAND

MEMORANDUM OF THE PROPOSALS OF THE IRISH DELEGATES

TO THE BRITISH REPRESENTATIVES

The Conferences to which you invited us "with a view to ascertaining how the association of Ireland with the community of nations known as the British Empire may best be reconciled with Irish National aspirations" have not up the the present produced a solution. You approach the problem without genuine realization of these National aspirations and in dealing with practical matters use descriptions which do not fit the objects. It is clear that if such an association is to be made possible the character and strength of Irish National aspirations must be realised, and that words and phrases must not obscure realities.

The nation is sacred and eternal to the mind and heart of the people of Ireland. Any attempt to dishonour or disrupt it is resented by the individual in Ireland with a more passionate intensity than he would resist attack upon himself. This fact, whatever view people of another nationality may hold of it is the dominating fact of Ireland, and no statesmanship can therefore leave it out of account. If Irish national aspirations are to be reconciled with the British community of nations, British statesmanship must keep the fact constantly before its mind that Ireland is no colony or dependency but an ancient and spirited nation.

Misdescription may often be honest in intention, but in the grave circumstances in which both bodies of representatives meet it is essential that every effort should be made to use no phrase which covers an unreality. The proposals made by the British Government on July 20th were officially described as "Dominion Status" - "Full Dominion Status" - "Free and equal partnership with the Nations of the British Commonwealth" and so forth. In reply to our questions at the Conference we find your proposals to mean that Ireland shall not possess the essential rights and powers which all the Dominions possess. We are not to have the control and defence of our coasts as all the Dominions have, nor to be sole judges of our own fiscal policy as they are; we are to bear a financial responsibility for your Imperial debt which they do not bear. The claim of Ireland is not Dominion Status but, if it were, your proposals would not confer that status.

Let us come to the realities. We sincerely desire to live in peace and amity with your country. We are convinced that if the warfare that has subsisted for seven centuries between two neighbouring nations can be ended, we shall have conferred a blessing on our respective peoples and have advanced the concord of mankind.

This can only be effected by a peace settlement which preserves the honour and interests of both countries. Your proposals, as they stand, give no basis for such a settlement. You desire to safeguard the security of your Empire. Ireland is resolved to achieve her freedom. With goodwill and good faith on both sides these purposes can undoubtedly be attained. We therefore offer you proposals for a Treaty which will ensure their realisation.

DÁIL ÉIREANN.

IRISH DELEGATION OF PLENIPOTENTIARIES.
SECRETARIAT.

Defence

1. Our unrestricted right & duty to provide for our own defence must be maintained. Otherwise we are lower even than a Dominion

2. No military occupation on their part (according to their pledge)

3. Any facilities to them to have a time-limit as short as possible.

4. Defence arrangements should not (subject to (3) above) limit our right (as of Dominions) to an independent voice in war & peace to be maintained

Note written by Erskine Childers to RCB on fundamental requirements for Defence. Negotiations in London

Handwritten note by Erskine Childers outlining what, in his view, should be the Irish position in relation to any discussions on defence matters. 'Our unrestricted right & duty to provide for our own defence must be maintained. Otherwise we are lower even than a Dominion.'

NAI PRIV 1093/4/3

R.C. Barton 2.D.

CHAIRMAN'S MINUTES OF SUB-CONFERENCES

on Novr. 2nd at Noon, and at 6.45 p.m.

Sub-Conference
at noon Novr 2nd
at Lord Birkenhead's
room- House of Lords.

Present:

Mr.Arthur Griffith
Mr.Michael Collins
Lord Birkenhead.

Mr.Collins and myself met Lord Birkenhead by arrangement in the forenoon at his rooms to hand him my letter
addressed to Mr. Lloyd George confirming my personal
assurances to the latter in my conversation on Sunday
night.

Lord Birkenhead asked whether I could not change the
word "with" to "within" in the phrase about Association
with the British Commonwealth.   I stated it could not
be done.   He also pointed out my phrase about "local
powers" for an Ulster area and said this would be read
by the Ulstermen to mean a detraction from their present
powers if they come under an All-Ireland Parliament.
He reminded me that I had stated we did not wish to
detract from their powers in such an event.   I agreed
that my phrase might be altered to make my meaning clear
to them, since, in his opinion, it was not sufficiently
so.
He then asked me to meet himself and Lloyd George
later. We agreed to do so and parted.

Sub-Conference
at 6.45 p.m.
Novr.2nd at
10 Downing Street.

Present :

Mr.Arthur Griffith) Mr.Lloyd George)
Mr.Michael Collins) Lord Birkenhead)

Mr.Austin Chamberlain subsequently
came in.

In the evening we met Lloyd George and Birkenhead by
arrangement at 10 Downing Street.   Chamberlain subsequently
came in.   They had a typewritten re-draft of my letter.
They stated they thought copies of this had been sent some
time before to me at Hans Place.   I think they were quite
genuine about this and that it was through an error it had
not been done.

The first alteration suggested ("with the other States
associated within the British Commonwealth",) I accepted
as it did not alter the essence of the formula.   They had
omitted the word "a" before "recognition of the Crown".
This we had restored.   The formula on Naval Defence they
desired to alter by the omission of "agreed to be". We had
a long conflict over this and matters approached a dead-
lock.   Finally the whole thing was re-drafted on a suggestion from Mr. Collins who secured the embodiment of the
quotation from their Memo., and we agreed on it as it now
stands.

(1) 11147961X

A smiling Michael Collins pictured
leaving 15 Cadogan Gardens.

Courtesy of the National Library of Ireland. NPA MKN40

Minutes of meetings held on 2 November 1921
between members of the two delegations
at the House of Lords at noon and at
10 Downing Street at 6.45pm. The key issues
of Ireland's future relationship with the
British Empire and partition loomed large.

NAI PRIV 1093/1/11

Opening page of Robert Barton's annotated copy of British proposals for a possible treaty, as presented to him by Thomas Jones. It is dated 16 November 1921.

NAI PRIV 1093/1/40

Most SECRET.

R. C. Barton 2.D.

The Unsigned Document

It is hereby agreed that :-

Dominion with a Parliament.

1. Ireland shall subject to the provisions hereinafter appearing have the status of a self-governing Dominion with a Parliament having powers to make laws for the peace order and good government of the whole of Ireland and an Executive responsible to that Parliament.

Status similar to that of Canada near as may be.

2. The position of Ireland in relation to the Imperial Parliament and Government and otherwise shall subject as aforesaid be assimilated as nearly as may be to that existing in the case of the Dominion of Canada.

Debt & War Pensions.

3. Ireland shall make contributions towards the service of the Public Debt of the United Kingdom and towards the payment of war pensions, the amount of such contributions being determined in default of agreement by the arbitration of one or more independent persons appointed from within His Majesty's Dominions.

England to have exclusive control of the Seas round Ireland pending arrangement for Ireland to defend herself.

4. Until an arrangement has been made between the British and Irish Governments providing for the establishment by Ireland of a Naval Force for the coastal defence of Ireland, the defence by sea of the British Islands, including Ireland, shall be undertaken exclusively by His Majesty's Imperial Forces.

Harbour & other facilities

5. The Irish Government shall at all times afford to His Majesty's Imperial Forces such harbour and other facilities as the British Government may require for the purpose of such defence as aforesaid.

(1)

PRIV1093/1/40 (2)

R. C. Barton T.D

CoṁAIRLe Feaḋmannaċ
na hÉireann.
IRISH DELEGATION OF PLENIPOTENTIARIES.

22, Hans Place S.W.

Nov. 23rd. 1921.

TO THE PRESIDENT.

A E, a Chara :

As arranged, Mr. Collins, Mr. Barton and myself met
Mr. Lloyd George, Mr. Chamberlain, and Lord Birkenhead at Downing
Street this morning.

Our Memorandum was the basis of discussion. On the
Crown they declared they had no alternative. They must fight. We
put up our counter-proposal briefly, but they declared it impossible.
On the Navy they were very strong, claiming that all facilities needed must be granted. It appeared as if they were claiming the
occupation of all or any of our ports for naval purposes. It trans-
pired later they were thinking of a state of war — not of a state
of peace. When this was cleared up, they moved towards us. One
the whole, there was a slight advance in our favour here.

On trade Lloyd George maintained his Free Trade atti-
tude, but it was fairly/explained what No.9 in the Memorandum *satisfactorily*
meant. It means, they say, merely that neither country shall
issue prohibition against the commodities of the other country, and
nothing more. This, however, would not prevent either country,
in cases of disease etc, closing its ports against the importation *etc*
of ~~its~~ diseased commodity.
the

complained that
On Ulster Lloyd George declared/that I had assured him
I would not let him down, if he put up the proposals subsequently
embodied in their memorandum to Craig, and we had not embodied them
in our memorandum. I said I had given him that assurance and I now
repeated it, but I told him at the time it was his proposal - not
ours. Therefore, it did not appear in our document. Our proposal
was, in our opinion, better but it was different.

He was satisfied. He had misunderstood us in this
instance and said as much. He would put his proposal to Craig
from himself only. He would like to consult privately with his
colleagues for a few minutes.

They then retired and consulted for a time. On their
return Lloyd George said that before he met Craig, he must know where
he stood on the fundamentals. If he had to fight on fundamentals,
there was no help for it, but it would be a tragedy if we broke up
on any verbal or technical misunderstandings. He suggested, therefore, that as myself and Mr. Collins had seen Lord Birkenhead
before I wrote the letter on which they had been acting, we should
do so again, and go over the document with him.

Lord Birkenhead suggested that we should bring a constitutional lawyer with us. We have arranged to meet him to-morrow
at 10.30 and bring Mr.Chartres with us. Lloyd-George has postponed his interview with Craig until 5 in the evening to await the
result, if any, of the meeting.

Do Chara,

(Signed) Art o Griobhtha.

A letter from Arthur Griffith to Éamon de Valera giving an account of a meeting at 10 Downing Street earlier that day, 23 November 1921. It records the British negotiators taking a firm line on the issues of concern to them. It also refers to Lloyd George's proposed boundary commission, which was eventually incorporated into the Treaty. 'On the Crown they declared they had no alternative. They must fight.'

NAI PRIV 1093/4/22

Éamonn Duggan and George Gavan
Duffy emerging from 10 Downing
Street during the negotiations.

Courtesy of UCD Archives P80-171

Partition was a key issue for the Irish
negotiators. They argued that the existing
territory of Northern Ireland could be
adjusted to reflect the reality of nationalist
majorities in certain areas that might wish
to come under the jurisdiction of a new Irish
state. This map, from Robert Barton's papers,
indicates the political geography of north-
east Ulster. It displays areas with populations
that, the negotiators argued, would be in
favour of, or opposed to, partition, delineated
according to local government districts.

NAI PRIV/1093/8/1

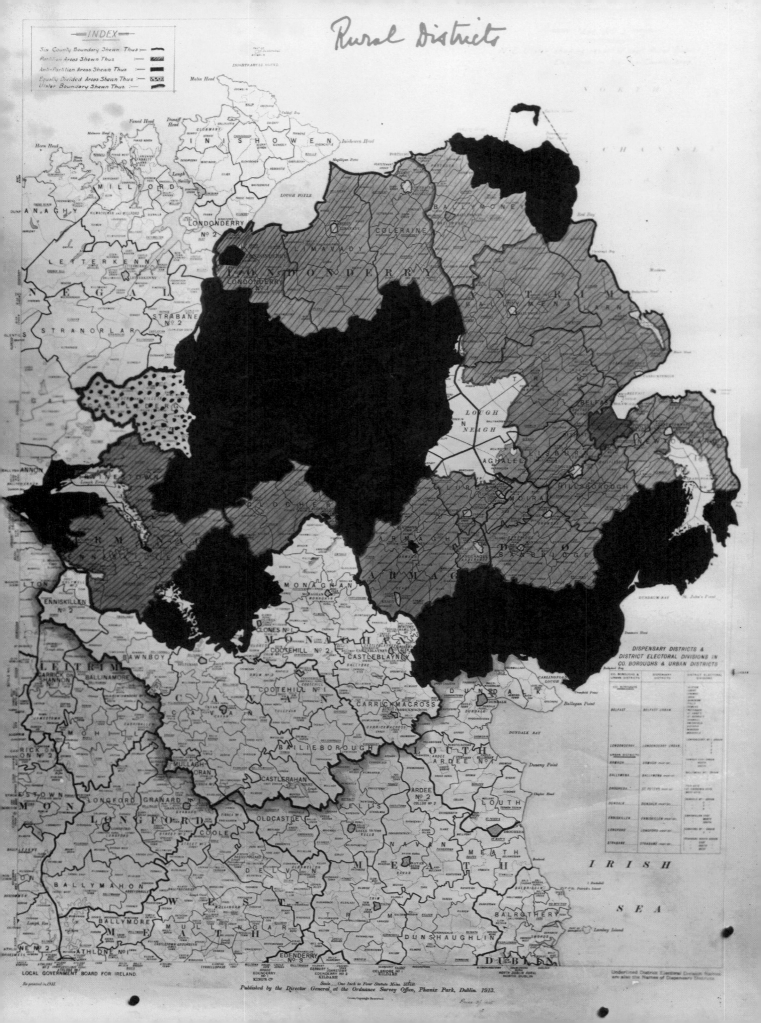

INDEX

Six County Boundary Shewn Thus
Partition Areas Shewn Thus
Anti-Partition Areas Shewn Thus
Equally Divided Areas Shewn Thus
Ulster Boundary Shewn Thus

DISPENSARY DISTRICTS &
DISTRICT ELECTORAL DIVISIONS IN
CO. BOROUGHS & URBAN DISTRICTS

LOCAL GOVERNMENT BOARD FOR IRELAND.

Scale — One Inch to Four Statute Miles.
Published by the Director General at the Ordnance Survey Office, Phœnix Park, Dublin. 1913.

Life in London

There was limited time for leisure amidst the delegation's busy schedule. Nonetheless, while detached from friends and family back home, the delegation experienced London life: living and working in Knightsbridge and Chelsea, shopping in Harrods, going to the theatre, attending religious services at the Brompton Oratory and St Luke's Chelsea and occasionally sightseeing. Lily O'Brennan noted in early November that it was quite possible that they would be in London until Christmas. Some members of the delegation, such as O'Brennan and Arthur Griffith, related their experiences of life in London when writing to family members in Ireland.

Members of the delegation in relaxed mood soon after their arrival in London, most likely in Hans Place. From left to right: Timothy Smiddy, May Duggan, Éamonn Duggan, Gerty Conry.

Courtesy of the National Library of Ireland. MS 49,835/15/10

'During the early days of the negotiations, Collins received many abusive and threatening letters from anonymous writers. These, of course, passed through my hands. One morning, I opened an envelope addressed to him containing a piece of cloth, and a letter enclosed stated that the cloth contained disease germs which the writer hoped would kill Collins and everyone near him.'

Éamon Broy recalls some of the hostility directed towards the Irish delegation in London
(Military Archives, Dublin, BMH WS 1280)

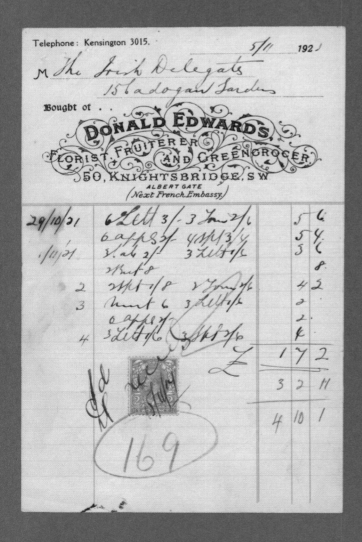

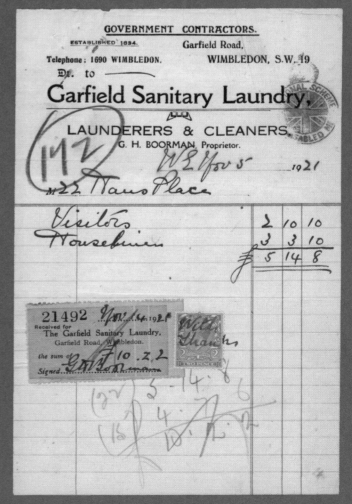

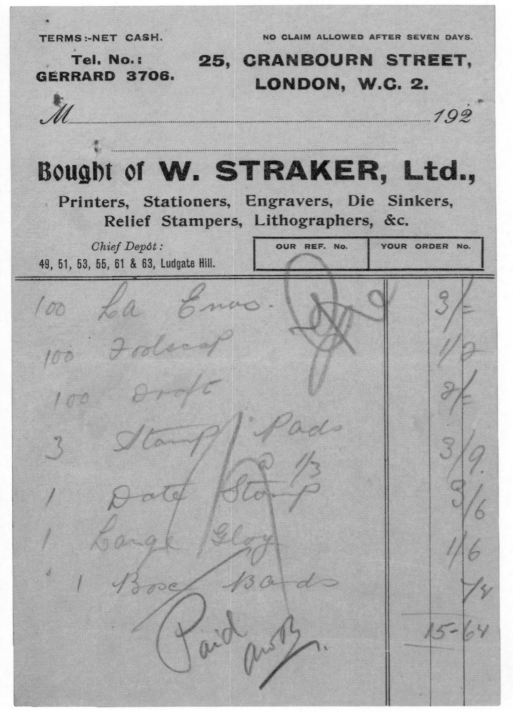

TERMS:-NET CASH.   NO CLAIM ALLOWED AFTER SEVEN DAYS.

Tel. No.:
GERRARD 3706.

25, CRANBOURN STREET,
LONDON, W.C. 2.

M_____ 192

Bought of **W. STRAKER, Ltd.,**

Printers, Stationers, Engravers, Die Sinkers,
Relief Stampers, Lithographers, &c.

Chief Depôt:
49, 51, 53, 55, 61 & 63, Ludgate Hill.

	OUR REF. No.	YOUR ORDER No.

100	La Envs.	3/=
100	Foolscap	1/2
100	Draft	2/=
3	Stamp Pads	3/9.
1	Date Stamp	3/6
1	Large Gloy	1/6
1	Box Bands	1/4
	Paid	15-64

Various receipts for everyday
items and services requested by
the Irish delegation.

NAI DE/3/1/169, 172, 53

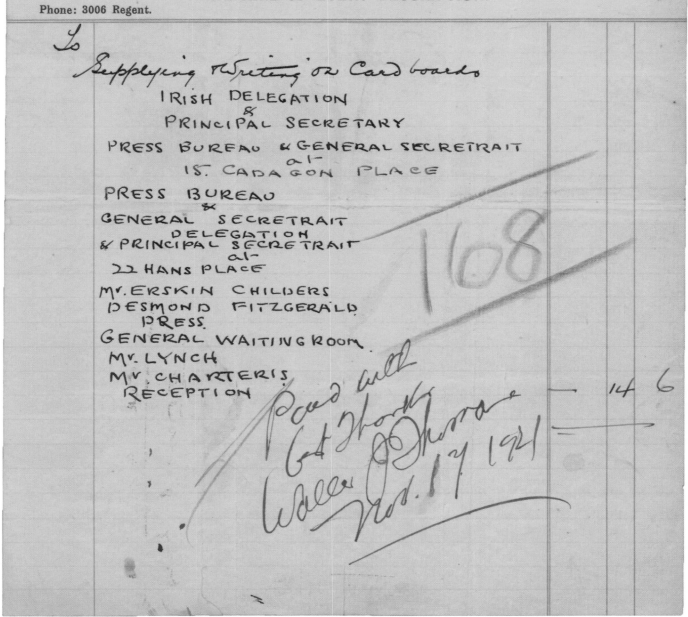

Miss O'Brien

Nov. 7 _____ 1921

Dr. to WALTER J. THOMAS,
Builder, Decorator, Sign Writer, Plumber & French Polisher,
19, YORK BUILDINGS, ADELPHI, W.C. 2.
REPAIRS OF EVERY DESCRIPTION.

Phone: 3006 Regent.

To

Supplying & Writing on Card boards
IRISH DELEGATION
&
PRINCIPAL SECRETARY
PRESS BUREAU & GENERAL SECRETRAIT
at
15. CADAGON PLACE

PRESS BUREAU
&
GENERAL SECRETRAIT
DELEGATION
& PRINCIPAL SECRETRAIT
at
22 HANS PLACE

Mr. ERSKIN CHILDERS
DESMOND FITZGERALD
PRESS
GENERAL WAITING ROOM
Mr. LYNCH
Mr. CHARTERIS
RECEPTION _____ 14 6

168

Paid with
Gt Thanks
Walter J Thomas
Nov. 17 1921

Invoice dated 7 November 1921 for official
signage displayed at both 15 'Cadogan Place'
(Cadogan Gardens) and 22 Hans Place.

NAI DE/3/1/168

Dáil Éireann.

Tórcaireact Feadmannac na hÉireann.

Oifig an Rúnaide.

IRISH DELEGATION OF PLENIPOTENTIARIES.

SECRETARIAT.

22 Hans Place S.W
8/11/21.

(1)

Dearest Fan;

I have just written to my mother, Maire & sent a
p.c to Ronan & E. O'Connor; but as I have a quiet sanctum
I am writing to you — I was going to put it off till tomorrow,
but it is so seldom that I have a quiet time I may as well
start off, even if I cannot finish it tonight.

Well, I am certain, if things get fixed up you
will easily get a decent position (R.C would think of
you, from one thing he said in the train — saying
would you like position of arbitrator) and in his
department clever heads will be required. You know
you got inferior work before, and it would be better
to wait 'the rising tide' and get scope. I am so
pleased about the Lecture Committee. Maire does not
correspond I would say at all except with E. too
I only answered her letter of the 27/10/21 just now.
I think she would like to come over but I am so
tied, but she would see a little of me — not much.
If she would be bothered with that. We had not
Hallow — Eve. That night I went to the Opera, but
the maids & waiters so held a Hallow Eve in the
kitchen — we had nothing to remind us.

Bob is very good to me. The parties have
now got into groups & I am in with David & him,
and I prefer that to anything. I am sure he
would love a letter. You should write & tell

The first two pages of a letter from Lily O'Brennan to her sister Áine Ceannt (widow of the
executed 1916 leader Éamonn Ceannt), dated 8 November 1921. She writes of various mutual
acquaintances, sightseeing in and around London. She went on to describe the progress of
the negotiations: 'Things are at a very critical stage at present... though on the other hand I
feel that if 10 days are got through or perhaps half that, we may be here til xmas'.

(2)

him about your trip to Gleann. He is always referring
to the 'Bulgar' &c and was asking for Ronan yesterday.
Mrs Phillpot asked me out to tea some evening. E's
two sisters are lovely but I succumbed entirely to
Mrs Davidson-Houston. Her husband was a Lt Col & killed in
the war. Both are very pretty. I never got to visit Mrs
Stopford yet but will go round some evening this week.
Just imagine Mrs Phillpot send malt extract (tonic) to E.
who would not take it & I wrote & said I would return
it. Bob made me take it & on Sunday just as we
were saying 'good-bye' she said perhaps he might take a
liquid tonic & that she would send round for it. I
gasped & said alright but as she was sending for
it early I realised I would not have time to
purchase another; so I whispered to David who
broke the news — Bob said nothing! We had a
great joke over it in Soho. E enjoyed the joke!
You can imagine how I felt at the critical moment.

I went for a long walk with Phylis on Saty
night. On Saturday afternoon E. Bob, David, & I motored to
the Crystal Palace in an open car. There was a
fruit show on & we had a lovely drive back.
It is a huge place built of glass by
Albert the Prince Consort & was in Hyde Park
& moved outside London later.

Members of the Irish delegation, most likely in Hans Place. Among those pictured are: Robert Barton (standing, far left), George Gavan Duffy (seated, centre), Éamonn Duggan (standing, third from right), May Duggan (seated, second from right), Desmond Fitzgerald (seated, far right), Lilly O'Brennan, (standing, third from left), Gerty Conry (seated, second from right), D.L. Robinson (standing, second from left), Timothy Smiddy (standing, second from right).

Courtesy of the National Library of Ireland. MS 49,530/27/6

Dáil Éireann.

Torcaireact Feadmannac na hÉireann.

Oifig an Rúnaide.

IRISH DELEGATION OF PLENIPOTENTIARIES.

SECRETAIRIAT.

1921

					Finance
Oct. 21.	Press Cuttings for Mr Collins	£ 2 . 2 . 0 ✓	Fin	—	4-12-1
"	Cable to New York for Mr. Collins.	1 . 16 . 1 ✓			
"	Telegram to President	1 . 3 .			
22	do. do.	1 . 9 .	✗		
24	Cable to New York for Mr Collins	14 . 0	Fin		
25	Envelopes	10 . 6			
"	Brush for Typewriter	9	Sty .	1-0-3	
Nov. 5	Wire Trays	6 . 0			
" 9	3rd Class rail Euston to Westland Row	2 . 15 . 11½	Travg.		
"	Cabin on Boat	4 . 6	W.O		
"	Taxis in Dublin.	5 . 0	W.O	12-15-1	
" 10	1st Class return North Wall to Euston	7 . 16 . 7½	W.O		
"	Sleeper on train	15 . 0	W.O		
"	Taxis	10 . 0	W.O		
"	Porterage re.	5 . 0	W.O		
		£18 . 7 . 5			

(156)

Received the sum of £18 . 7 . 5 .

Finance 4 - 12 · 1   Diarmuid Ó hÉigceartuigh

Sty .   1 - 0   3

Travg Exs 12 - 15 - 1

18 - 7 - 5

14/11/21

Handwritten receipt for the reimbursement of various expenses incurred in October and November 1921, signed by Diarmaid O'Hegarty.

NAI DE/3/1/1/156

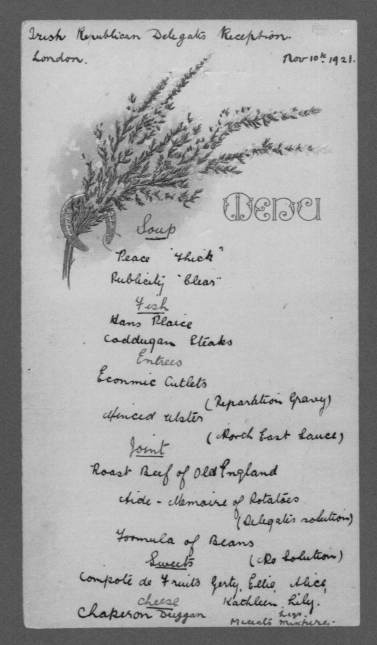

Handwritten menu card for a party held at Hans Place on 10 November 1921. The items on the menu were given satirical names. The event apparently culminated in Michael Collins and other members of the IRA and IRB having a food fight and throwing coal at one another.

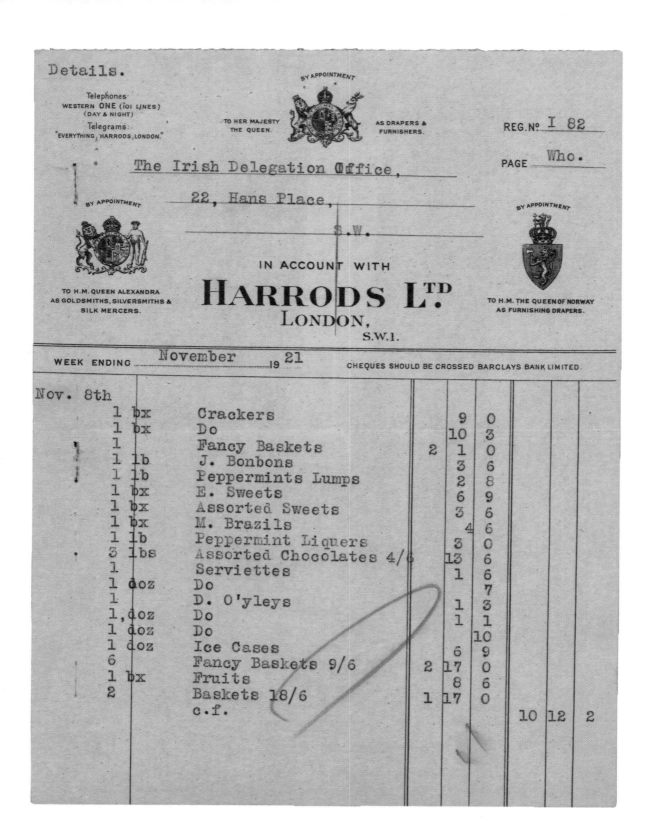

Details.

Telephones:
WESTERN ONE (101 LINES)
(DAY & NIGHT)
Telegrams:
"EVERYTHING, HARRODS, LONDON."

BY APPOINTMENT
TO HER MAJESTY
THE QUEEN.

AS DRAPERS &
FURNISHERS.

REG. No. I 82

PAGE Who.

The Irish Delegation Office,

22, Hans Place,

S.W.

BY APPOINTMENT

TO H.M. QUEEN ALEXANDRA
AS GOLDSMITHS, SILVERSMITHS &
SILK MERCERS.

IN ACCOUNT WITH

HARRODS L^{TD}
LONDON,
S.W.1.

BY APPOINTMENT

TO H.M. THE QUEEN OF NORWAY
AS FURNISHING DRAPERS.

WEEK ENDING _____ November _____ 19 21   CHEQUES SHOULD BE CROSSED BARCLAYS BANK LIMITED.

Nov. 8th

1 bx	Crackers			9	0	
1 bx	Do			10	3	
1	Fancy Baskets	2	1	0	0	
1 lb	J. Bonbons		3	6		
1 lb	Peppermints Lumps		2	8		
1 bx	E. Sweets		6	9		
1 bx	Assorted Sweets		3	6		
1 bx	M. Brazils		4	6		
1 lb	Peppermint Liquers		3	0		
3 lbs	Assorted Chocolates 4/6		13	6		
1	Serviettes		1	6		
1 doz	Do			7		
1	D. O'yleys		1	3		
1 doz	Do		1	1		
1 doz	Do			10		
1 doz	Ice Cases		6	9		
6	Fancy Baskets 9/6	2	17	0		
1 bx	Fruits		8	6		
2	Baskets 18/6	1	17	0		
	c.f.				10	12	2

Invoice from Harrods addressed to the Irish delegation's offices
at Hans Place for goods supplied from 8 to 10 November 1921,
presumably for the party held on 10 November.

NAI DE/3/1/273

I 82 Who		Brought Forward					10	12	2

Date / Qty	Item	£	s	d	£	s	d
Nov. 8th							
	To Hire of Candilabra	1	2	6			
	Candlestick		18	0			
12	Bon Bon Dishes		4	0			
					2	4	6
Nov. 9th							
	Boors		3	6			
2	Blowouts		1	6			
2	Streamers		2	6			
3	Blowouts		1	0			
1	C. Joke			5			
1	Joke			2			
2	Balloon		1	0 6			
1	Raifle			6			
1	Flag			4½			
1	Clapper			4			
1	Bag Ball			9			
3	Tambor 1/6		4	6			
2	Blowouts		1	4			
2	Cigars @ 3d			6			
3 yds	Muslin @ 1/0½		3	1½			
3 yds	Do @ 1/0½		3	1½			
	Cards		1	4			
					1	5	5½
Nov. 10yh							
6	Trumpet		1	0			
3	Rattles		1	0			
1	Fish		1	0			
3	Blowouts			9			
4	Clappers		1	0			
	Ball Room Powder		1	9 6			
1 doz	Menus		4	6			
						11	0
					14	13	1½

DÁIL ÉIREANN.

AIREACT AIRGID	Department of Finance
ÁT-CLIAT.	DUBLIN.

Dear Mollie

Tell Ita I'm very sorry for the poor Rabbit. I'll try to get her another one or a dog like him if she'll take care of him and get rid of her cold. I hope Nevin is well and that he can practise all the conjuring tricks. If I can get time one day I'll see if there are any more in London

The two houses here are not sufficient for the number of people over — some are staying in hotels near by. Besides the delegates and the three secretaries, there are Messrs Milroy, M'Carthy, M'Grath (T. D's) Several experts on Economics, Law, &c, five typists, several Clerks, and Mrs Duggan and Mrs Smith-Gordon. Some days we are at work all day long. For instance, yesterday I was working from 11 a.m to half past one in the morning. Other days are quite slack. The weather here is turning foggy. There is nobody named Mrs Schultz here nor do I know anything of her. If we are here to the end of this week. Come over please with Dr. Fogarty who writes he is coming, and stay at least for a few days

Yours
. Arthur

22/11/21

Letter to Maud 'Mollie' Griffith from her husband Arthur Griffith, written from London on 22 November 1921. Griffith writes of his hope that she might join him in London and expresses sorrow over the death of his daughter's pet rabbit. He also provides her with various details of life in London and the work of the delegation.

Courtesy of the National Library of Ireland. MS 49,530/8/3

'Meetings of the Delegation were held in Hans Place, but Collins carried on his functions as Director of Intelligence in Grosvenor House in Cadogan Gardens. He and Dermot O'Hegarty were there and Emmet Dalton, Tom Cullen, Broy and a number of others. Collins took all these over himself, partly by way of protection and partly by way of keeping in touch with things at home. They were passing backwards and forwards with information all the time. Remember, you could not trust even the postman, the King's messenger'.

Robert Barton recalls some of the living and working arrangements of the delegation
(Military Archives, Dublin, BMH WS 979)

The final days

Towards the end of the negotiations, Ireland's proposed relationship to the Crown and British Empire became the biggest obstacle to overcome.

The British side set a deadline of Tuesday 6 December to agree on a set of final proposals. Irish proposals to align with, rather than come into, the British Empire met with a hostile response; Griffith was told that no British government could accept this. Discussions intensified and consequently Griffith requested that a Cabinet meeting be held in Dublin on Saturday 3 December. This necessitated another journey back to Ireland, made longer for most of the delegates when the mailboat *Cambria*, on which they travelled, collided with a schooner in the Irish Sea, killing three of the schooner's crew. Griffith had travelled earlier but the rest of the delegation arrived in Dublin on Saturday morning.

The Cabinet meeting on the afternoon of Saturday 3 December was acrimonious but its members resolved that the delegates should return to make a final effort to secure key concessions. The Cabinet agreed that if these were not forthcoming, the delegates would refuse to accept the British proposals and would let the Dáil decide on them instead. The plenipotentiaries embarked upon the long return journey to London that evening.

Letter from Arthur Griffith to Éamon de Valera, dated 29 November, informing him of recent developments and requesting an urgent meeting of the Dáil Cabinet in Dublin. 'No British Government could attempt to propose to the British people the abrogation of the Crown.'

NAI PRIV/1093/4/14

R.-C. Barton 2.D.

22, Hans Place S.W.
29/11/21.

THE PRESIDENT.

A E, A Chara :

Last night (Monday) Mr. Duggan and myself at Lloyd George's request went to Chequers to meet Lloyd George.

We met him there with Lord Birkenhead and Sir Robert Horne, Chancellor of the Exchequer.

They declared the document we had sent in earlier, w was impossible for them. No British Government could attempt to propose to the British people the abrogationm of the Crown. It would be smashed to atoms.

We told them we had no authority to deal with them on any other basis than the exclusion of the Crown from purely Irish affairs. We then entered into a general discussion in which they knocked out my argument in the document we sent in - that the Crown in the Dominions was merely a symbol but in Ireland a reality - by offering to put in any phrase in the Treaty we liked to ensure that the function of the Crown in Ireland should be no more in practice than it is in Canada or any Dominion.

On the Oath of Allegiance which we instanced in part of the conversation, they said, though it was an immense difficulty for them, they would try to modify it, if that would help us. On the "elective head" of the Irish State they pointed out that the "elective head" of any State is the Premier. They guaranteed that any nominal head would be only appointed in consultation with the Irish Ministry. In reply to our questions, they guaranteed he would have no power - be merely a symbol, and that no one would ever be appointed to whom the Irish Ministry offered any objection.

To-day by appointment M.C., Duggan and myself met Lloyd George, Birkenhead, and Chamberlain at Downing Street. They confirmed the conversation of the previous evening and specifically offered to put a phrase in the Treaty ensuring that the Crown should have no more authority in Ireland than in Canada. They offered us a form of Oath of Allegiance different from their one, which we stated would not do. We raised the question of Defence and Trade.

They proposed to send their final proposals to Craig and ourselves on Tuesday. We objected. We should see them beforehand. They agreed to send us them on Thursday evening, but formally to hand them to us on Tuesday.

It is essential a Cabinet meeting should be held. I shall return to Dublin on Friday morning and hope to see you on that evening. Please have a Cabinet meeting arranged for Saturday morning, when we shall be all there. I intend to return to London on that evening.

Mise, Do Chara,

a.g.

MEETING OF CABINET AND DELEGATION 3rd DECEMBER, 1921.

'In reply to a question by Minister of Defence [Cathal Brugha] as to who was responsible for the splitting of the Delegation so that two Members (Messrs. Griffith and Collins) did most of the work and that the other members were not in possession of full information it was stated that the British Government was responsible for the arrangement but it had the approval of the whole delegation. The Minister of Defence here remarked that the British Government selected its men. On the motion of Mr. Griffith this remark was withdrawn.'

Secretary's notes of meeting of the cabinet and delegation held 3 December 1921 (NAI DE 2/304/1)

MEETING OF CABINET.

25th NOVEMBER. 1921.

(a) The following formula was unanimously approved:-

"That Ireland shall recognise the British Crown for
the purposes of the Association as symbol and
accepted head of the combination of Associated States".

(b) Vote of annual voluntary sum to Civil List unanimously
approved.

MEETING OF CABINET AND DELEGATION.

3rd DECEMBER, 1921.

VIEWS OF DELEGATES.

(a) Mr. Griffith in favour of Treaty. Refused to break on
question of Crown and thereby hand to Ulster the position
from which she had been driven.

(b) Mr. Barton of opinion that England's last word had not
been reached and that she could not declare war on question
of Allegiance. The Treaty would not give Dominion Status
nor any guarantee re Ulster. Would vote against acceptance.

(c) Mr. Gavan Duffy agreed with Mr. Barton that England was
bluffing and that the Irish proposals, with small reservations on Defence etc., could be obtained. Would like the
Treaty to be rejected by An Dail and sent back amended.
Said "No" definitely to Treaty.

(d) Mr. Duggan agreed with Mr. Griffith. Believed Treaty to be
England's last word and would not take responsibility of
saying "No".

(e) Mr. Collins was in substantial agreement with Messrs. Griffith
and Duggan. The non-acceptance of Treaty would be a gamble as
England could arrange a war in Ireland within a week. Sacrifices
to N.E. Ulster made for sake of essential unity and justified.
With pressure further concessions could be obtained on Trade and
Defence. Oath Allegiance would not come into force for 12
months - question was, therefore, would it be worth while taking
that 12 months and seeing how it would work. Would recommend that
Dail go to country on Treaty, but would recommend non-acceptance
of Oath.

(f) Mr. Childers of opinion that Par. 6 of Treaty would give Ireland
no national status. Sec. 7 (b) was important also as it meant
that when England went to war she would bring Ireland with her.

(g) In reply to a question by Minister of Defence as to who was
responsible for the splitting of the Delegation so that two
Members (Messrs. Griffith and Collins) did most of the work

Typescript copy of minutes of the meeting of the full Dáil Cabinet,
including plenipotentiaries, at the Mansion House, Dublin, on
3 December 1921. It records the views of those present on the content
of a draft treaty and the debate on its terms as they then stood.

NAI DE/2/304/1/80

and that the other members were not in possession of full information it was stated that the British Government was responsible for the arrangement but it had the approval of the whole Delegation.

The Minister of Defence here remarked that the British Government selected its men.

On the motion of Mr. Griffith this remark was withdrawn.

MEETING OF CABINET.

3rd DECEMBER, 1921.

(a) In the course of a lengthy discussion of the Treaty the President gave it as his opinion that it could not be accepted in its then form. He personally could not subscribe to the Oath of Allegiance nor could he sign any document which would give N.E. Ulster power to vote itself out of the Irish State. With modifications, however, it might be accepted honourably, and he would like to see the plenipotentiaries go back and secure peace if possible. He believed the Delegates had done their utmost and that it now remained to them to show that if document not amended that they were prepared to face the consequences - war or no war. He would deal with present document exactly as with that of 20th July - say it cannot be accepted and put up counter proposals.

(b) Mr. Griffith did not like the document but did not think it dishonourable. It would practically recognise the Republic and the first allegiance would be to Ireland. If it were rejected the people would be entitled to know what the alternative is. The country would not fight on the question of allegiance and there would be a split. He would not recommend the Government to accept but would say that the Plenipotentiaries should sign and leave it to President and Dail to reject.

(c) The Minister for Defence was in perfect agreement with President, the only matter upon which he could disagree would be the question of recognising the King of England as Head of the Associated States.

(d) Document does not guarantee essential unity of Ireland.

MEETING OF CABINET AND DELEGATION.

3rd DECEMBER, 1921.   (resumed)

(a) Mr. Griffith would not take the responsibility of breaking on the Crown. When as many concessions as possible conceded, and when accepted by Craig, he would go before the Dail. The Dail was the body to decide for or against war.

(b) The President took his stand upon last Irish proposals which meant external connection with the Crown. He suggested the following amendment to the Oath of Allegiance:-

"I......do solemnly swear true faith and allegiance to the constitution of the Irish Free state, to the Treaty of Association and to recognise the King of Great Britain as Head of the Associated States."

(c) Delegates to carry out their original instructions with same powers.

(d) Delegation to return and say that Cabinet wont accept Oath of Allegiance if not amended and to face the consequences, assuming that England will declare war.

(e) Decided unanimously that present Oath of Allegiance could not be subscribed to.

(f)
(f) Mr. Griffith to inform Mr. Lloyd George that the document could not be signed, to state that it is now a matter for the Dail, and to try and put the blame on Ulster.

(g) On a majority vote it was decided that the Delegation be empowered to meet Sir James Craig if they should think necessary. The following voted for and against:-

FOR: President, Finance, Foreign Affairs, Economics and Local Government.

AGAINST : Defence and Home Affairs.

(h) It was decided that the President would not join the Delegation in London at this stage of the Negotiations.

Colm O Murchadha.

ar son Runaidhe na hAireachta.

Recd @ 10 pm (or so)
Wednesday 30th Nov 1921

? Constitutional

CONFERENCE ON IRELAND.

PROPOSED ARTICLES OF AGREEMENT.

1. Ireland shall have the same national status in the Community of Nations known as the British Empire as the Dominion of Canada, the Commonwealth of Australia, the Dominion of New Zealand, and the Union of South Africa, with a Parliament having powers to make laws for the peace order and good government of Ireland and an Executive responsible to that Parliament, and shall be styled and known as the Irish Free State.

? advantage

2. Subject to the provisions hereinafter set out the position of the Irish Free State in relation to the Imperial Parliament and Government (and otherwise) shall be assimilated to that of the Dominion of Canada, *and constitutional as* and the law and practice governing the exercise in relation to the Dominion of Canada of the powers of the Crown or the representative of the Crown and of the Imperial Parliament shall govern the exercise of those powers in relation to the Irish Free State.

relationship of the Crown

Make the veto as nominal as in Canada Any words that will express that

3. The representative of the Crown in Ireland shall be a Governor-General appointed in like manner as the Governor-General of Canada and in accordance with the practice observed in the making of such appointments.

4. The oath to be taken by members of the Parliament of the Irish Free State shall be in the following form:-

I .... solemnly swear to bear true faith and allegiance to the Constitution of the Irish Free State; to the Community of Nations known as the British Empire; and to the King as the Head of the State and of the Empire.

To go into the appendix

①

-1-

The opening pages of two drafts of the proposed Treaty, showing how the document evolved in the final days of the negotiations. The first, dated 30 November, has been annotated by Collins and Griffith. The second text was used at one of the final meetings between the delegations on 5 December 1921. The fourth article was altered in red ink, apparently by Lord Birkenhead, as the Irish negotiators objected to the use of the term British Empire.

NAI DE/2/304/1/83/13, NAI PRIV 1093/4/30

S.F.C.30.

PROPOSED ARTICLES OF AGREEMENT.

1. Ireland shall have the same constitutional status in
the Community of Nations known as the British Empire as the
Dominion of Canada, the Commonwealth of Australia, the
Dominion of New Zealand, and the Union of South Africa,
with a Parliament having powers to make laws for the peace
order and good government of Ireland and an Executive
responsible to that Parliament, and shall be styled and
known as the Irish Free State.

2. Subject to the provisions hereinafter set out the
position of the Irish Free State in relation to the
Imperial Parliament and Government and otherwise shall be
that of the Dominion of Canada, and the law, practice and
constitutional usage governing the relationship of the
Crown or the representative of the Crown and of the
Imperial Parliament to the Dominion of Canada shall govern
their relationship to the Irish Free State...

3. The representative of the Crown in Ireland shall be
a Governor-General appointed in like manner as the Governor-
General of Canada and in accordance with the practice
observed in the making of such appointments.

4. The oath to be taken by members of the Parliament
of the Irish Free State shall be in the following form:-

> I............do solemnly swear true faith and
> allegiance to the Constitution of the Irish
> Free State as by law established and that I
> will be faithful to H.M. King George V., his
> heirs and successors by law, in virtue of the
> common citizenship of Ireland with Great Britain
> and her adherence to and membership of the group
> of nations forming the British Commonwealth of Nations.

137

An Irish response to some of the British proposals, dated 4 December 1921 and annotated by members of the Irish delegation

NAI PRIV 1093/4/46

Completed by RCB C&D &EC
for Delegation conference
+ amended by AG MC &ED

 τoτ̄cαιρεαċτ ροαḋṁαννaċ
na hÓιρεαnn.
IRISH DELEGATION OF PLENIPOTENTIARIES

Suggested Amendments
to

PROPOSED ARTICLES OF AGREEMENT.   Dec - 4 · 1921

1. The Legislative, executive and judicial authority of Ireland shall be derived exclusively from the Elected Representatives of the Irish people.

11. Ireland will agree to be associated with the British Commonwealth for all purposes of common concern, including defence, peace and war, and political treaties, and to recognise the British Crown as Head of the Association.

111. As a token of that recognition, the Irish legislature will vote an annual contribution to the King's personal revenue.

1V. In matters of common concern, the rights and status of Ireland shall be in no respect less than those enjoyed by any of the component States of the British Commonwealth represented in the League of Nations.   There shall be between Ireland and these States such concerted action, founded on consultation, as the several Governments may determine.

The oath to be taken by members of the Irish Parliament shall be in the following form:—

V. I do ~~solemnly~~ swear to bear true faith and allegiance to the Constitution of Ireland and to the Treaty of Association of Ireland with the British Commonwealth of Nations, and I recognize King George V as Head of the ~~Association~~ States

V1. Ireland shall assume liability for such a portion of the Public Debt of Gt.Britain and Ireland existing at the date hereof and of the war pensions existing at that date as may be fair and equitable, having regard to any just claims on the part of Ireland by

way of set off or counter claim, the amount of such
sums being determined in default of agreement by the
arbitration of one or more independent persons being
citizens of the British Empire.

Vll. (1) As an associated State, Ireland recognises the
obligation of providing for her own defence by sea,
land, and air, and of repelling by force any attempt
to violate the integrity of her shores and territorial
waters, and in the common interest

(2) For five years, pending the establishment of
Irish Coastal Defence forces,facilities for the
coastal defence of Ireland shall be afforded to the
British Government as follows :-

(a) In time of peace such harbour and other
facilities as are indicated in the Annex A.
hereto, or such other facilities as may
from time to time be agreed between the
British Government and the Government of
the Irish Free State .

(b) In time of war such harbour and other
facilities as the British Government may
require for the purposes of such defence
as aforesaid.

8. With a view to securing the observance of the principle
of international limitation of armaments, if the
Government of the Irish Free State establishes and
maintains a local military defence force, the establishments thereof shall not exceed in size such proportion of the military establishments maintained

(2)

139

in Great Britain as that which the population of
Ireland bears to the population of Great Britain.

A convention for Free Trade

9.   For a period of ten years no protective customs
duties shall be imposed in Great Britain on Irish
goods nor in Ireland on British goods, but this

This must be
embodied in
a separate
Convention.
    provision shall not be construed as preventing
the imposition of customs duties designed to prevent dumping or other unfair competition.

Provided that nothing contained in this article
shall be construed to prevent the Irish Government from taking measures for the encouragement
of infant industries, or for the economic development of Ireland.

I object but because I am a Bolshevist
I object to your putting me in a position where I shall have
to stand for a superior class against an inferior sic

Statement by MC.
taken down by me at
time it was made namely
whilst we were discussing
this Draft

(3)

DÉIL 1092/4/ 46(3)

10.   A Convention shall be made between the British
and Irish Governments for the regulation of
civil communication by air.

11.   The Government of Ireland agrees to pay fair
compensation on terms not less favourable than
those accorded by the Act of 1920 to judges,
officials, members of Police Forces
and other Public Servants who are discharged by
it or who retire with its approbation in consequence of the change of Government effected
in pursuance hereof.

Provided that this agreement shall not apply
to members of the Auxiliary Police Force or
to persons recruited in Great Britain for the
Royal Irish Constabulary during the two years
next preceding the date hereof.

The British Government will assume responsibility
for such compensation or pensions as may be
payable to any of these excepted persons.

(4)

Concluding the Treaty

On 4 December the British negotiators prepared to break off the talks.

Duffy had candidly admitted that membership of the British Empire was the main difficulty for the Irish delegation. This was the one issue over which there was likely to be a breach with the British side. Duffy's admission undermined the Irish strategy of linking any breakdown in the negotiations to the issue of partition.

The imminent collapse was averted as Griffith hastily arranged a meeting between Collins and Lloyd George for the next morning, 5 December.

The delegations met that afternoon to address any final issues. When Collins pointed out that any association with the British Empire would only be acceptable if concessions on Irish unity were forthcoming, Lloyd George surprised Griffith and the others by referring to Griffith's private willingness to consider a boundary commission to adjudicate on the border with Northern Ireland. Griffith had originally agreed not to officially reject this British proposal in order to protect Lloyd George from unionist critics within the Conservative Party with which he shared power, but it was now used to remove any prospect of the Irish plenipotentiaries breaking off the negotiations over partition. Griffith agreed he would sign the proposed treaty. Lloyd George responded that any refusal to sign by the other plenipotentiaries would automatically lead to a renewed conflict.

The Treaty was signed in 10 Downing Street at 2.15am on 6 December 1921. The two sets of negotiators shook hands and the meeting concluded at 2.20am.

Opening page of the minutes of a meeting, held at short notice to avert a breakdown in the talks, between Michael Collins and David Lloyd George on 5 December.

NAI DE/4/5/7

MR. MICHAEL COLLINS' MINUTE OF HIS INTERVIEW WITH
MR. LLOYD GEORGE AT 10, DOWNING STREET AT 9.30 a.m
MONDAY, DECEMBER 5th., 1921

----oOo----

Arising out of Mr. Jones' conversation with Mr. Griffith,
the latter indicated to me last night that Mr. Lloyd George desired
to see me.   This conversation took place subsequent to the
official conference held at 10, Downing Street on Sunday evening
at 5 p.m.   I did not attend this conference for the reason that
I had, in my own estimation, argued fully all points.   This
morning Mr. Griffith came to me again and suggested in his official
capacity as Chairman of the Delegation that I should have the
meeting with Mr. Lloyd George as so much depended on the Delegation
at this vital time.   Mr. Jones had suggested the interview for
9.15, but as I had not made up my mind until after speaking to
Mr. Griffith this morning I did not see Mr. Lloyd George until
9.30 as stated above.

Acting on the general resumé of points of difference as
sketched by me at the Cabinet Meeting on Saturday, 3rd instant,
I had my points set out as follows :-

(1) The essential unity of Ireland.   Suggestion that we
        should press for a letter from Craig indicating
        either :

        (a) Acceptance of Conditions, and naming those
             Conditions.

        (b) Rejection.

(2) Oath of Allegiance.   Clause 4 of British Document.

(3) Defence. Clause 6 and Annex A. of British Document
        (29a) - date 1st December.

(4) Trade. Clauses 9 and 10 of ditto.

CONFERENCE ON IRELAND.

MR. GRIFFITH'S NOTES OF TWO SUB - CONFERENCES HELD ON
December 5th/December 6th. 1921 at 10, DOWNING STREET.
No.1 - at 3 p.m.
No.11 - at 11.30 p.m. to 2.30 a.m.

_____

Present:

BRITISH REPRESENTATIVES	IRISH REPRESENTATIVES
Mr.Lloyd George	Mr.A.Griffith
Mr.Chamberlain	Mr.M.Collins
Lord Birkenhead	Mr.R.C.Barton
Mr.Churchill	

The following is the barest outline of what happened
on Monday- 5th.December. We were there all day and prob-
ably half the night - with a couple of breaks.

Mr.Barton is making, at my request, a long Memo.
of events, which we shall bring with us for you to-morrow
night.

Things were so strenuous and exhausting that the
sequence of conversation is not in many cases clear.in my
mind to-day.

Mr.Barton, Mr.Collins and myself were on our side.
Mr.Lloyd George, Birkenhead, Churchill and Chamberlain
on theirs.

The Conference opened with the British Delegates
in a bad mood. They had had a full Cabinet meeting pre-
viously and apparently had had a rough time.

Lloyd George began by suggesting we had let him
down over the Ulster proposals.

We denied this and argued we must have a reply
from Craig refusing or accepting these proposals before
we proceeded.

The others pointed out that as they were prepared
to go ahead with their proposals irrespective of Craig
there was no ground for our contention.

We went on this line of argument for a while when
Lloyd George declared we were trying to bring about a
break on Ulster. The question was,would we or would we
not come within the community of nations known as the
British Empire. The question must be answered because
it was the question of peace or war.

(1)

I was determined not to let them break on the Crown as I told you at the Cabinet meeting. The decision of peace or war had to be made.

I said, provided we came to agreement on other points, I would accept inclusion in the Empire on the basis of the Free State. After that they went on and gave way on Fiscal autonomy wholly, yielded more on defence and some minor matters.

Then they asked me whether I spoke for myself or for the delegation. I said I spoke for myself. They then said they were standing together as a unit. We should do the same. We adjourned.

Later on we met again. We had discussed the matter and decided our course.

We returned and proposed other amendments. They accepted most of them when we said we spoke as a united delegation, that we were willing to recommend inclusion with the other States in the Empire. It was on this basis, by the way, that they altered the oath of allegiance.—— earlier in the day.

At 2.15 a.m. we signed the document.

This is a very hasty and imperfect sketch of what happened in a prolonged conference on four occasions during which it was on the point of bursting to fragments.

Arthur Griffith's notes of the two sub-conferences held between the British and Irish delegations on 5–6 December 1921 at 10 Downing Street, culminating in the signing of the Treaty at 2.15am on 6 December.

NAI DE/2/304/1/90

'<u>LLOYD GEORGE</u> stated that he had always taken it that Arthur Griffith spoke for the Delegation, that we were all plenipotentiaries and that it was now a matter of peace or war and we must each of us make up our minds…

<u>LLOYD GEORGE</u> stated that he would have to have our agreement or refusal to the proposals by 10 p.m. that evening.'

Notes by Robert Barton of two sub-conferences held on 5–6 December, 1921 at 10 Downing Street (NAI DE 2/304/1)

A page from Robert Barton's notes of the meeting between the delegations on 5 December 1921 at 10 Downing Street, in which David Lloyd George threatened war if the Treaty were not signed.

NAI DE/2/304/1/91

LLOYD GEORGE stated that he had always taken it that
Arthur Griffith spoke for the Delegation, that we were
all plenipotentiaries and that it was now a matter of
peace or war and we must each of us make up our minds.
He required that every Delegate should sign the document
and recommend it, or there was no agreement. He said
that they as a body had hazarded their political future
and we must do likewise and take the same risks. At
one time he particularly addressed himself to me and
said very solemnly that those who were not for peace
must take the full responsibility for the war that
would immediately follow refusal by any Delegate to
sign the Articles of Agreement.

He then produced two letters one of which he
said he must that night send to Craig. One was a
covering letter to H. M. Government's proposals for
the future relations of Ireland and Great Britain and
stated that the Irish Delegation had agreed to
recommend them for acceptance by Dail Eireann. The
other stated that the Irish Delegation had failed to
come to an agreement with H. M. Government and therefore he had no proposals to send to Craig.
LLOYD GEORGE stated that he would have to have our
agreement or refusal to the proposals by 10 p.m. that
evening. That a special train and destroyer were ready
to carry either one letter or the other to Belfast and
that he would give us until ten o'clock to decide.

'LLOYD GEORGE got excited. He shook his papers in the air, declared that we were trying deliberately to bring about a break on Ulster because our people in Ireland had refused to come within the Empire and that Arthur Griffith was letting him down where he had promised not to do so.'

Notes by Robert Barton of two sub-conferences held on 5–6 December, 1921 at 10 Downing Street
(NAI DE 2/304/1)

9.

> There was a discussion amongst ourselves
> lasting from 9 to 11.15 at 22 Hans Place
> at which a decision was eventually reached
> to recommend the Treaty to the Dail.

SUB-CONFERENCE No. II.

11.15 p.m. - 2.20 a.m

At 11.30 we returned to Downing Street and attacked the document again. We endeavoured to get Clause 3 removed, but failed. We however succeeded in getting the word "Governor-General" out, it being left to us to decide upon a term. The title "President," Chamberlain stated, was inadmissible.

MICHAEL COLLINS demanded and secured the removal of the word "local" as a prefix to the Irish Free State's military defence force.

They agreed to the verbal changes in financial clause 5. CHAMBERLAIN took exception to the "if anys" going in, as he said it was too late to quibble over such small points. We pointed out that Clause 9 was still left intact and that it should have been removed under the agreement on 8. LLOYD GEORGE said that it referred to transport only. It meant ships entering harbours and that there must be provision to prevent boycotting of English shipping. BIRKENHEAD said that the wording of the clause was ambiguous now that the compulsory Free Trade clause was gone and suggested redrafting it. This was done immediately.

MICHAEL COLLINS required the removal of Clause 14 (e). (the Ulster Army) and that its substance be got into the safeguards for Ulster clause. This was agreed to.

'<u>LLOYD GEORGE</u> then asked whether we as a Delegation were prepared to accept these Articles of Agreement and to stand by them in our Parliament as they as a Delegation would stand by them in theirs.

<u>Arthur Griffith</u> replied 'We do.'

Notes by Robert Barton of two sub-conferences held on 5–6 December, 1921 at 10 Downing Street
(NAI DE 2/304/1)

Robert Barton's account of the final meeting between the two sides on 5–6 December 1921, culminating in the signing of the Treaty.

NAI DE/2/304/1/91

10.

MICHAEL COLLINS queried the reference to summoning

of the Southern-Ireland Parliament in Clauses 15 &

17, and BIRKENHEAD immediately drafted an explanatory

memorandum as follows:-

> "It is intended by Clauses 15 and 17
> to make it plain that the functions
> therein referred to shall be discharged by
> the Provisional Government of Southern
> Ireland and that for that purpose a
> transfer shall be made by them of the
> necessary powers under the Government of
> Ireland Act, 1920, as soon as the mutual
> ratifications have been exchanged. The
> Provisional Government will it is
> contemplated upon such ratification
> undertake the Govt. of S. Ireland
> immediately until the necessary Acts in
> both Parliaments confer upon it the
> statutory authority contemplated in
> this instrument.
>
> "B."

LLOYD GEORGE then asked whether we as a Delegation were

prepared to accept these Articles of Agreement and to

stand by them in our Parliament as they as a Delegation

would stand by them in theirs.

ARTHUR GRIFFITH replied, "We do."

WE then discussed the release of the prisoners and
procedure for ratification and other matters whilst
awaiting the final draft.

The final draft was read over, agreed to
and signed; also the Annex.

THE BRITISH DELEGATION lined up to shake
hands and say goodbye, and the Conference ended at
2.20 a.m. on December 6th.

---

months from the date hereof.

18.   This instrument shall be submitted forthwith by His
Majesty's Government for the approval of Parliament and by
the Irish signatories to a meeting summoned for the
purpose of the members elected to sit in the House of
Commons of Southern Ireland, and if approved shall be
ratified by the necessary legislation.

Decr 6th 1921

On behalf of the
British Delegation

D Lloyd George

Austen Chamberlain

Birkenhead.

Winston S. Churchill

L. Worthington Evans

Hamar Greenwood

Gordon Hewart.

On behalf of the Irish
Delegation

.

Mícheál Ó Coileáin

Riobárd Bartún.

E. S. Ó Dugáin

Seórsa Gabháin Uí Dhubhthaigh.

Who signed the Treaty?

The Treaty was initially signed only by those present at the final meeting in 10 Downing Street in the early morning of 6 December 1921.

The first signatories were Griffith, Collins and Barton on the Irish side and Lloyd George, Birkenhead, Chamberlain and Churchill on the British side. The members of the delegation who had gone to Downing Street returned with the Irish copy of the text to Hans Place at 2.45am and the last two plenipotentiaries – Duggan and Duffy – signed it there. Based on the description of the document given by Kathleen McKenna, this is the document retained today in the National Archives in Dublin.

Later, on the morning of 6 December, Duggan took the document to Dublin. In the afternoon Thomas Jones called at Hans Place seeking the remaining signatures of the Irish plenipotentiaries on the British copy. Griffith was apparently going to sign on Duggan's behalf when Daniel McCarthy, who was also part of the delegation, recalled that he had Duggan's signature on a copy of a programme from the Royal Albert Hall event on 26 October. This was cut out and pasted onto the British text; the outline was clearly visible in the facsimiles released to the press. Duffy was the last of the plenipotentiaries to sign the British copy of the Treaty.

Daniel McCarthy recalled that he had Duggan's signature on a copy of a programme from the Royal Albert Hall event on 26 October. This was cut out and pasted onto the British text; the outline was clearly visible in the facsimiles released to the press.

Courtesy of the National Archives of the UK DO/118/51

'The lights in the hall, too, were dim when, at about 2.45 a.m. [on] 6 December, the arrival of the cars and the ring on the hall-door brought Tom and myself running to open it. One by one the men entered. Collins was not with them; he had gone directly to Cadogan Gardens, as had Desmond FitzGerald. Diarmuid O'Hegarty was holding the Treaty document rolled around, scroll-like, in both his hands. He moved towards the telephone table, unrolled it, and displayed it with the ink signatures fresh, almost still damp, on it. The others stood nearby gazing at the two columns of signatures.

Slowly, Duggan, his eyes fixed on the document, a cigarette between his lips, unscrewed the cap of his fountain-pen, and in bold calligraphy, added his signature, E. S. Ó Dugain. Gavan Duffy was the last of the Delegates to sign, in his miniature hand-writing: Seórsa Ghabháin Uí Dhubhthaigh.

The column of Irish signatures was headed in Arthur Griffith's hand-writing: 'On behalf of the Irish Delegation', beneath he had signed himself Art Ó Griobhta, and in parenthesis Arthur Griffith. The first column contained the signatures of D. Lloyd George, Austen Chamberlain, Birkenhead and Winston Churchill. The signatures of L. Worthington-Evans, Hamar Greenwood and Gordon Hewart were not as yet affixed. The date, first typed December 5 1921 was corrected, in ink, to 6. The names of the secretaries, Thomas Jones and Lionel Curtis for the British and Erskine Childers and John Chartres for the Irish were in type on the fly-leaf.

The die was cast: my tension relaxed. I broke down and cried softly.'

Kathleen Napoli-McKenna,
A Dáil girl's revolutionary recollections (Dublin, 2014)

The Anglo-Irish Treaty
of 6 December 1921

The Treaty, more properly called the 'Articles of Agreement', gave Ireland a form of independence as the Irish Free State, a self-governing dominion in the British Empire with the same status as Canada. It became a member, along with Canada, Australia, New Zealand and South Africa, of a grouping of states within the Empire that were now officially called the British Commonwealth of Nations.

The Irish Free State established by the Treaty was one of many states to emerge after the First World War. The new state was distinctive as it emerged from under the rule of one of the powers that had been victorious in the war, rather than any of Europe's defeated empires. Dominion status was a considerable step forward from the Home Rule demanded by Irish nationalists before the First World War, but it was not the fully independent republic sought by many who had fought for Irish independence.

The Treaty ended 120 years of direct British rule over 26 of Ireland's 32 counties. Technically the Treaty established a 32-county state but Ireland had been partitioned into two jurisdictions by the Government of Ireland Act, 1920. Northern Ireland had been formally established on 3 May 1921 and was ruled by a devolved government. The Treaty permitted Northern Ireland to opt out of the jurisdiction of the Irish Free State, which it did. Provisions in the Treaty to establish a boundary commission and a north-south Council of Ireland in which the parliaments in Belfast and Dublin could meet gave Irish nationalists hopes for unity. The Council of Ireland was never established and such hopes were ultimately unfulfilled.

The Treaty also addressed Anglo-Irish trade, British military and naval requirements, financial obligations and the right of the new Irish state to establish some limited military and naval forces.

Ultimately views of the Treaty revolved around the question of sovereignty, of who had the ultimate power of governance in Ireland: the British monarch or the people of Ireland.

The Anglo-Irish Treaty, formally described as the 'Articles of Agreement', signed by the Irish and British delegates in London, 6 December 1921.

NAI TSCH 2002/5/1

<u>T R E A T Y</u>.

between

<u>GREAT BRITAIN & IRELAND</u>.

signed

<u>6th December,1921</u>.

at <u>LONDON</u>.

Article 1:

The new state would be called the 'Irish Free State' and would have the same constitutional status within the British Empire as Canada, Australia, New Zealand and South Africa (informally known as the 'white dominions').

Article 2:

The status of the Irish Free State within the British Empire was specifically designated to be the same as that of Canada, which was a concession intended to reassure the Irish negotiators.

Article 3:

The representative of the Crown in Ireland was to be appointed in the same way as the governor-general of Canada.

Article 4:

Members of the Irish Free State's parliament were to swear an oath pledging allegiance to its constitution and fidelity to the monarch (this article contains the first official use of the term 'British Commonwealth of Nations'). The oath of fidelity to the monarch, popularly known as the 'oath of allegiance', was a significant cause of discontent in Ireland.

S E C R E T.

PROPOSED ARTICLES OF AGREEMENT.

1.   Ireland shall have the same constitutional status in the Community of Nations known as the British Empire as the Dominion of Canada, the Commonwealth of Australia, the Dominion of New Zealand, and the Union of South Africa, with a Parliament having powers to make laws for the peace order and good government of Ireland and an Executive responsible to that Parliament, and shall be styled and known as the Irish Free State.

2.   Subject to the provisions hereinafter set out the position of the Irish Free State in relation to the Imperial Parliament and Government and otherwise shall be that of the Dominion of Canada, and the law, practice and constitutional usage governing the relationship of the Crown or the representative of the Crown and of the Imperial Parliament to the Dominion of Canada shall govern their relationship to the Irish Free State.

3.   The representative of the Crown in Ireland shall be appointed in like manner as the Governor-General of Canada and in accordance with the practice observed in the making of such appointments.

4.   The oath to be taken by Members of the Parliament of the Irish Free State shall be in the following form:-

> I.......do solemnly swear true faith and allegiance to the Constitution of the Irish Free State as by law established and that I will be faithful to H.M.King George V., his heirs and successors by law, in virtue of the common citizenship of Ireland with Great Britain and her adherence to and membership of the group of nations forming the British Commonwealth of Nations.

1.

5.   The Irish Free State shall assume liability for the service of the Public Debt of the United Kingdom as existing at the
date hereof and towards the payment of war pensions as existing
at that date in such proportion as may be fair and equitable, having regard to any just claims on the part of Ireland by way of
set off or counter-claim, the amount of such sums being determined in default of agreement by the arbitration of one or more
independent persons being citizens of the British Empire.

6.   Until an arrangement has been made between the British and
Irish Governments whereby the Irish Free State undertakes her
own coastal defence, the defence by sea of Great Britain and Ireland shall be undertaken by His Majesty's Imperial Forces. But
this shall not prevent the construction or maintenance by the Government of the Irish Free State of such vessels as are necessary
for the protection of the Revenue or the Fisheries.

        The foregoing provisions of this Article shall be reviewed
at a Conference of Representatives of the British and Irish
Governments to be held at the expiration of five years from the
date hereof with a view to the undertaking by Ireland of a share
in her own coastal defence.

7.   The Government of the Irish Free State shall afford to His
Majesty's Imperial Forces:-

        (a) In time of peace such harbour and other facilities as
            are indicated in the Annex   hereto, or such other
            facilities as may from time to time be agreed between
            the British Government and the Government of the Irish
            Free State; and

                                2.

Article 5:
The Irish Free State was to
assume an agreed liability
for Britain's public debt
and some war pensions.

Article 6:
The Royal Navy would retain
responsibility for Irish coastal
defence for at least the next
five years, though the Irish
Free State could possess
revenue or fisheries protection
vessels. This and subsequent
articles reflected British
concerns about their maritime
security and naval power.

Article 7:
The Royal Navy would retain
defended anchorages around
the Irish coastline (specified in
the annex) and were entitled
to the use of further facilities
during wartime or in periods
of international tension.

Article 8:

The Irish Free State could establish its own military forces, though their size relative to the population could not exceed that of their British equivalents.

Article 9:

British and Irish ports were to remain open to each country's shipping traffic on payment of port dues.

Article 10:

The Irish Free State was to pay compensation to any public servants who might retire or lose their jobs due to the handover of power. This did not apply to members of the paramilitary 'Black and Tans' or Auxiliary Cadets.

(b)   In time of war or of strained relations with a Foreign Power such harbour and other facilities as the British Government may require for the purposes of such defence as aforesaid.

8.   With a view to securing the observance of the principle of international limitation of armaments, if the Government of the Irish Free State establishes and maintains a military defence force, the establishments thereof shall not exceed in size such proportion of the military establishments maintained in Great Britain as that which the population of Ireland bears to the population of Great Britain.

9.   The ports of Great Britain and the Irish Free State shall be freely open to the ships of the other country on payment of the customary port and other dues.

10.   The Government of the Irish Free State agrees to pay fair compensation on terms not less favourable than those accorded by the Act of 1920 to judges, officials, members of Police Forces and other Public Servants who are discharged by it or who retire in consequence of the change of government effected in pursuance hereof.

Provided that this agreement shall not apply to members of the Auxiliary Police Force or to persons recruited in Great Britain for the Royal Irish Constabulary during the two years next preceding the date hereof.   The British Government will assume responsibility for such compensation or pensions as may be payable to any of these excepted persons.

3.

11.   Until the expiration of one month from the passing of the
Act of Parliament for the ratification of this instrument, the
powers of the Parliament and the government of the Irish Free
State shall not be exercisable as respects Northern Ireland and
the provisions of the Government of Ireland Act, 1920, shall,
so far as they relate to Northern Ireland remain of full force
and effect, and no election shall be held for the return of
members to serve in the Parliament of the Irish Free State for
constituencies in Northern Ireland, unless a resolution is
passed by both Houses of the Parliament of Northern Ireland in
favour of the holding of such election before the end of the said
month.

12.   If before the expiration of the said month, an address
is presented to His Majesty by both Houses of the Parliament
of Northern Ireland to that effect, the powers of the Parliament and Government of the Irish Free State shall no longer
extend to Northern Ireland, and the provisions of the Government
of Ireland Act, 1920, (including those relating to the Council
of Ireland) shall so far as they relate to Northern Ireland, continue to be of full force and effect, and this instrument shall
have effect subject to the necessary modifications.

      Provided that if such an address is so presented a Com-
mission consisting of three persons, one to be appointed by
the Government of the Irish Free State, one to be appointed by
the Government of Northern Ireland and one who shall be Chairman to be appointed by the British Government shall determine
in accordance with the wishes of the inhabitants, so far as may
be compatible with economic and geographic conditions, the bound-
aries between Northern Ireland and the rest of Ireland, and for
the purposes of the Government of Ireland Act, 1920, and of this
instrument, the boundary of Northern Ireland shall be such as
may be determined by such Commission.

                        4.

Article 11:
The jurisdiction of the Irish Free State would not apply to Northern Ireland until one month after the Treaty was formally ratified.

Article 12:
If Northern Ireland chose to opt out of the Irish Free State before this month had passed, a boundary commission would be appointed to determine the final border between the Irish Free State and Northern Ireland.

13.   For the purpose of the last foregoing article, the powers
of the Parliament of Southern Ireland under the Government of
Ireland Act, 1920, to elect members of the Council of Ireland
shall after the Parliament of the Irish Free State is constituted be exercised by that Parliament.

14.   After the expiration of the said month, if no such address
as is mentioned in Article 12 hereof is presented, the Parliament and Government of Northern Ireland shall continue to exercise as respects Northern Ireland the powers conferred on them
by the Government of Ireland Act, 1920, but the Parliament and
Government of the Irish Free State shall in Northern Ireland
have in relation to matters in respect of which the Parliament
of Northern Ireland has not power to make laws under that Act
(including matters which under the said Act are within the
jurisdiction of the Council of Ireland) the same powers as in
the rest of Ireland, subject to such other provisions as may be
agreed in manner hereinafter appearing.

15.   At any time after the date hereof the Government of Northern Ireland and the provisional Government of Southern Ireland
hereinafter constituted may meet for the purpose of discussing
the provisions subject to which the last foregoing article is
to operate in the event of no such address as is therein mentioned being presented and those provisions may include:

(a) Safeguards with regard to patronage in Northern Ireland:
(b) Safeguards with regard to the collection of revenue
    in Northern Ireland:
(c) Safeguards with regard to import and export duties af-
    fecting the trade or industry of Northern Ireland:
(d) Safeguards for minorities in Northern Ireland:

5.

(e) The settlement of the financial relations between
     Northern Ireland and the Irish Free State.

(f) The establishment and powers of a local militia in
     Northern Ireland and the relation of the Defence Forces
     of the Irish Free State and of Northern Ireland res-
     pectively:

and if at any such meeting provisions are agreed to, the same
shall have effect as if they were included amongst the provisions subject to which the Powers of the Parliament and
Government of the Irish Free State are to be exercisable in
Northern Ireland under Article 14 hereof.

16.   Neither the Parliament of the Irish Free State nor the
Parliament of Northern Ireland shall make any law so as
either directly or indirectly to endow any religion or pro-
hibit or restrict the free exercise thereof or give any pre-
ference or impose any disability on account of religious belief or religious status or affect prejudicially the right
of any child to attend a school receiving public money without attending the religious instruction at the school or
make any discrimination as respects state aid between schools
under the management of different religious denominations or
divert from any religious denomination or any educational
institution any of its property except for public utility
purposes and on payment of compensation.

17.   By way of provisional arrangement for the administration of Southern Ireland during the interval which must
elapse between the date hereof and the constitution of a
Parliament and Government of the Irish Free State in accord-
ancetherewith, steps shall be taken forthwith for summoning
a meeting of members of Parliament elected for constituencies

6.

Article 16:
Neither parliament in
either the Irish Free State
or Northern Ireland were to
pass laws favouring any one
religion or discriminating
on the grounds of religious
belief, especially in
relation to education.

Article 17:
A 'provisional government'
was to be established to act
as a transitional authority
until the Irish Free State
formally came into existence
on 6 December 1922.

in Southern Ireland since the passing of the Government of Ireland Act, 1920, and for constituting a provisional Government, and the British Government shall take the steps necessary to transfer to such provisional Government the powers and machinery requisite for the discharge of its duties, provided that every member of such provisional Government shall have signified in writing his or her acceptance of this instrument. But this arrangement shall not continue in force beyond the expiration of twelve months from the date hereof.

18. This instrument shall be submitted forthwith by His Majesty's Government for the approval of Parliament and by the Irish signatories to a meeting summoned for the purpose of the members elected to sit in the House of Commons of Southern Ireland, and if approved shall be ratified by the necessary legislation.

On behalf of the Irish
Delegation

Art Ó Gríobhta (Arthur Griffith)

Mícheál Ó Coileáin

Riobárd Bartún

Eudmonn S. Ó Dugáin

Seóirse Gabhán Uí Dhubhthaigh

December 6, 1921.

On behalf of the British Delegation

D Lloyd George

Austen Chamberlain

Birkenhead

Winston S. Churchill

7.

ANNEX .

1.   The following are the specific facilities required.

Dockyard port at Berehaven.

(a) Admiralty property and rights to be retained as at the date
     hereof. Harbour defences to remain in charge of British
     care and maintenance parties.

Queenstown.

(b) Harbour defences to remain in charge of British care and main-
     tenance parties. Certain mooring buoys to be retained for
     use of His Majesty's ships.

Belfast Lough.

(c) Harbour defences to remain in charge of British care and
     maintenance parties.

Lough Swilly.

(d) Harbour defences to remain in charge of British care and
     maintenance parties.

Aviation.

(e) Facilities in the neighbourhood of the above Ports for coastal
     defence by air.

Oil Fuel Storage.

(f) Haulbowline) To be offered for sale to commercial companies
) under guarantee that purchasers shall maintain
    Rathmullen) a certain minimum stock for Admiralty purposes.
)

2.   A Convention shall be made between the British Government and the

Government of the Irish Free State to give effect to the following

conditions:-

(a) That submarine cables shall not be landed or wireless sta-
     tions for communication with places outside Ireland be estab-
     lished except by agreement with the British Government; that
     the existing cable landing rights and wireless concessions
     shall not be withdrawn except by agreement with the British
     Government; and that the British Government shall be entitled
     to land additional submarine cables or establish additional
     wireless stations for communication with places outside Ireland.

(b) That lighthouses, buoys, beacons, and any navigational marks
     or navigational aids shall be maintained by the Government
     of the Irish Free State as at the date hereof and shall not
     be removed or added to except by agreement with the British
     Government.

(c) That war signal stations shall be closed down and left in
     charge of care and maintenance parties, the Government of the
     Irish Free State being offered the option of taking them over
     and working them for commercial purposes subject to Admiralty
     inspection, and guaranteeing the upkeep of existing telegraphic
     communication therewith.

3.   A Convention shall be made between the same Governments for the

regulation of Civil Communication by Air.

8.

L. Worthington Evans

Hamar Greenwood

Gordon Hewart.

The LNWR mailboat *Scotia* docked at Holyhead,
1903, with railway tracks clearly visible
alongside the wharf; the train terminal was
located at the harbour. The *Scotia* operated
between Dún Laoghaire and Holyhead on the
Irish Sea route. Such links by sea and by rail
were the means by which the Treaty delegation
made their way to London and back again
between October and December 1921.

The immediate aftermath

The main nationalist daily newspapers in Ireland welcomed the signing of the Treaty with extensive coverage, including the full text of the document itself. The unionist press in Northern Ireland struck a more cautious note. King George V was, according to the official telegram he sent to Lloyd George, 'overjoyed'. The prime minister himself was reportedly 'jubilant'.

International reaction to the signing of the Treaty was positive, though not in the die-hard British Tory press. The full text of the Treaty was printed across the front page of the *New York Times* of 7 December 1921. News of its signing, covered dramatically on its front page the previous day, pushed a congressional message by President Warren Harding to the inside pages.

Britain's friends and foes across the globe studied the news from London, as did members of the growing independence movements across the British Empire. The Irish diaspora, which had bankrolled Dáil Éireann since 1919, also began to have its say. Support within the diaspora was by and large positive, but concern and discontent over the so-called oath of allegiance and the continuance of partition were recurring themes, particularly in the Irish community in the United States.

In London the offices of the Irish delegation were swiftly cleared out as the delegation prepared to return home. Most of the delegation left London just before 9pm on Wednesday 7 December.

They were seen off by thousands of supporters at Euston Station; Michael Collins even lost his hat in the throng. They arrived in Dún Laoghaire early the next morning, to be greeted by more crowds and an IRA guard of honour before travelling to the Gresham Hotel for breakfast.

On 8 December 1921, the Dáil Cabinet assembled in the Mansion House, Dublin, from 12pm to 9.30pm and narrowly approved the Treaty by four votes to three. De Valera, who opposed the Treaty, issued a statement to the press outlining his position. A public meeting of the Dáil to debate the Treaty was summoned. The debate began in the council chamber of University College Dublin (UCD) on Dublin's Earlsfort Terrace on 14 December 1921.

A letter from Arthur Griffith to David Lloyd George dated 6 December 1921 informing him of a forthcoming meeting with southern unionist representatives. 'We desire to secure the willing cooperation of Unionists in common with all other sections of the Irish nation in raising the structure and shaping the destiny of the Irish Free State.'

NAI DE/2/304/1/88/26

Ꞇorcaireaꞔꞇ ꝼeaꝺmannaꞔ
na héireann.
IRISH DELEGATION OF PLENIPOTENTIARIES

SECRET.

22, Hans Place S.W

6th. December, 1921.

To:
THE RIGHT HONOURABLE DAVID LLOYD GEORGE,
        10, Downing Street, S.W.

Sir :

I write to inform you that at a meeting I had
with the Representatives of the Southern Unionists
I agreed that a scheme should be devised to give them
their full share of representation in the First
Chamber of the Irish Parliament, and that as to the
Upper Chamber we will consult them on its constitution
and undertake that their interests will be duly represented.
        I wish also to take this occasion to say
that we desire to secure the willing cooperation of
Unionists in common with all other sections of the Irish
nation in raising the structure and shaping the destiny
of the Irish Free State. We look for their assistance
in the same spirit of understanding and goodwill which
we ourselves will show towards their traditions and
interests.

        I am, Sir,

        Yours faithfully,

        Signed -Arthur Griffith.

22, Hans Place S.W.
6th. December 1921.

THE PRESIDENT.

A E, a Chara :

  Mr Gavan Duffy and myself met Mr. Lloyd
George to-day. He said Parliament would be summoned
for Wednesday week and ratifying resolutions passed.
After that, if DAIL EIREANN ratified, the provisional
Government would be set up. Subsequently an Act
would be passed in ratification. No amendment would
be accepted to the resolution or the Act. The Treaty
would have to stand intact except by an agreement
between us. After the ratifying resolutions, the
internees would be immideiately released, and on
the setting up of the provisional Government, both
sides could pass an Act of Amnesty which would secure
the release of all our prisoners and the stoppage of
all prosecution for any offences in the war. This
was the procedure followed in South Africa.

  We pressed strongly for the release,
without delay, of the internees. He seemed inclined
but afraid of the strength of his military element
in opposition to it until the Treaty is ratified
by us. He is consulting his Cabinet on the matter
to-morrow.

      Mise, Do Chara,

     Oifig an Uaċcaráin

DEC 7 1921

Éamon de Valera at Strand House, Limerick, on the morning of 6 December 1921, having just received news of the signing of the Treaty. Back row, left to right: Mary Rynne (née O'Mara), Michael Rynne, Richard Mulcahy. Front row, left to right: Éamon de Valera, Stephen O'Mara (whose home this was), Cathal Brugha.

Courtesy of National University of Ireland Galway and the Rynne family.
NUIG P133220

A letter from Arthur Griffith to Éamon de Valera dated 6 December 1921 describing a meeting with David Lloyd George that day about the steps required to implement the Treaty.

NAI DE/2/304/1/88/28

Foreground, left to right: George Gavan
Duffy, Robert Barton and Arthur Griffith at an
unspecified location during the journey back
to Dublin after the signing of the Treaty.

'Mr Griffith would recommend document on basis of its merits – the remaining members on basis of signature'.

Cabinet minutes, 8 December 1921
(NAI DE 1/3)

164.

Meeting of Cabinet & Delegation

1. Recommendation of Treaty.

   Present: Pres. F.A., Fin., Econ. H.A.,
   Def., Loc.Gov., Asst. Loc. Gov.,
   Messrs. Duggan, Gavan Duffy,
   Childers & DOH.

   Duration of Meeting: 12 noon to
   9.30 pm. with 2 adjournments.

2. President's Statement.

3. Summoning of Dáil.

8th Decr. 1921.

1. Following a discussion of the terms
   of the Treaty the following members
   declared in favour of recommending
   it to the Dáil : —
   A.Griffith, M.Collins, R. Barton, ~~bettes~~
   & W. Cosgrave, & K.O'Higgins (no vote)

   Mr. Griffith would recommend doc-
   -ument on basis of its merits —
   the remaining members on basis of
   signature.

   The following declared against
   recommending Treaty to Dáil:
   President, Cathal Brugha & A. Stack.

2. The Pres. to issue a statement to the
   press defining his position & that of
   the Min. of H.A. & Def.

3. A Public Session of Dáil to be summoned
   for Wed. 14th Dec. at 11. am Mansion House
   Ministers to remain in charge of their
   Depts. in meantime.

Minutes of the Dáil Cabinet meeting held in
Dublin on 8 December 1921, at which the Treaty
was accepted by four votes to three. Éamon de
Valera was among those who rejected it.

NAI DE1/3

The council chamber in the UCD buildings on
Earlsfort Terrace, Dublin, which was the venue
for the Dáil debate on the terms of the Treaty.

The meeting of DÁIL ÉIREANN to deal with the Peace Treaty began in the Council Chamber, University College, Dublin, on Wednesday December 14th, 1921.

Dáil Debates, Vol. T No. 2, 14 December 1921

Michael Collins arriving at Earlsfort Terrace during the Treaty debate.

Courtesy of the National Library of Ireland. INDH103

Crowds gathered outside UCD on Dublin's Earlsfort
Terrace during the Dáil debate on the Treaty, which
began on 14 December 1921.

Selected further reading

Dictionary of Irish Biography (online at www.dib.ie).

John Crowley, Donal Ó Drisceoil and Mike Murphy (eds), John Borgonovo (associate ed.), *Atlas of the Irish Revolution* (Cork, 2017).

Ronan Fanning, Michael Kennedy, Dermot Keogh and Eunan O'Halpin (eds), *Documents on Irish Foreign Policy. Vol I: 1919–1922* (1998) (online at www.difp.ie).

Ronan Fanning, *Fatal Path: British government and Irish revolution, 1910–1922* (London, 2013).

Tommy Graham, Brian Hanley, Darragh Gannon, Grace O'Keeffe (eds), *The split: from Treaty to Civil War, 1921–23* (Dublin, 2021).

Thomas Jones, *Whitehall diary, Vol. III: Ireland, 1918–1925*, ed. Keith Middlemas (Oxford, 1971).

Nicholas Mansergh, *The unresolved question: the Anglo-Irish settlement and its undoing, 1912–72* (New Haven, 1991).

Kathleen Napoli-McKenna, *A Dáil girl's revolutionary recollections* (Dublin, 2014).

Mícheál Ó Fathartaigh and Liam Weeks (eds), *The Treaty: Debating and establishing the Irish state* (Newbridge, 2018).

Exhibition details

Preview exhibition:
The British Academy,
10–11 Carlton House Terrace,
London,
12–23 October 2021

Main exhibition:
Coach House Gallery,
Dublin Castle Gardens,
Dame St,
Dublin 2
7 December 2021–27 March 2022.

Virtual tour:
nationalarchives.ie/2021commemorationprogramme/treaty-virtual-tour/

Acknowledgements

The exhibition on which this catalogue is based, *The Treaty, 1921: Records from the Archives*, was hosted by the British Academy in London in October 2021 and by the Office of Public Works in Dublin Castle between December 2021 and March 2022. It was supported by the Department of Tourism, Culture, Arts, Gaeltacht, Sport and Media under the Decade of Centenaries 2012-2023 Programme.

The National Archives would like to extend special thanks to the following individuals and organisations for assistance in the creation of this catalogue.

National Archives Treaty Exhibition Team
Zoë Reid
Elizabeth McEvoy
Suzanne Bedell
Rosemary King
Linda Tobin

National Archives Commemoration Programme Steering Group
Orlaith McBride
Zoë Reid
Linda Tobin
Niamh McDonnell
Hazel Menton
Natalie Milne
Melissa Collins
Antoinette Doran

National Archives Commemoration Programme Manager
Karen Downey

The National Archives, UK
Jeff James
Patricia Humphries
Dr Neil Johnston

National Library of Ireland
Dr Sandra Collins
Katherine McSharry
Bríd O'Sullivan
Ciara Kerrigan
Anne Brady

National Print Museum
Carla Marrinan
Mary Plunkett

NUI Galway
Dr Barry Houlihan

Mercier Archive
Mary Feehan

The Military Archives, Dublin
Commandant Daniel Ayiotis
Lisa Dolan

Royal Irish Academy
Dr John Gibney
Dr Michael Kennedy
Dr Kate O'Malley
Ruth Hegarty
Liz Evers

UCD Archives
Kate Manning

Phil Behan and family
Ruth Bourke
Liz Gillis
The Lynch family
The Montgomery family
Fiona Murray
Teresa Napoli McKenna
Rose Mary O'Brien
Eilish Rafferty
Professor Eda Sagarra
Elina Sironen

About the editors

John Gibney is Assistant Editor with the Royal Irish Academy's *Documents on Irish Foreign Policy* (DIFP) series. He is a graduate of Trinity College, Dublin, and was formerly a postdoctoral fellow at the University of Notre Dame and at NUI Galway. He has worked extensively in tourism and in the heritage and publishing sectors and has written widely on modern and early modern Irish history and historiography. He is the co-author (with Kate O'Malley) of *The Handover: Dublin Castle and the British withdrawal from Ireland, 1922* (Royal Irish Academy, 2022).

Zoë Reid is Keeper of Public Services and Collections at the National Archives. She is an accredited conservator and established the Conservation Department in the National Archives (Ireland) in 2002. She has been responsible for safeguarding the long-term preservation of the national collection and ensuring safe public access to the archives. Over the past 20 years she has presented her work at international conferences and been published widely in conservation journals.

Cover design

The cover design was created as part of collaboration with the National Print Museum. The design used is from a letterpress print created with assistance from letterpress printer Mary Plunkett using Gaelic type from the National Print Museum's collection. This design is inspired by the Dáil Éireann letterhead which is set in gaelic type. It can be found on a range of documents featured throughout this publication.

A series of limited-edition letterpress posters with seminal quotes from the book were also created and displayed at the book launch event in the State Apartments in Dublin Castle.

Cover images: Arthur Griffith, Courtesy of the National Library of Ireland. KE238, David Lloyd George, © National Portrait Gallery, London. NPG x168994